THE PRICE OF

FREEDOM

A True Story

Printed In Canada

Cover artwork by **Lucian Web Service**
Edited by **Myrna Tetz, Simon and Melanie Ivascu**
Pre-editor: **Marilyn Melashenko**
Print Set Up by **dittos Office Services Inc.**

General Notice: The names used in this book have been changed to protect the people involved. The author names and their families are accurate.

Some quotations were used from the songs:
" 'Till The Storm Passes By" by Mosie Lister and
" Because He Lives" by William J. Gaither/ Gloria Gaither

Additional copies of this book are available by visiting:
www.freedomsingers.com

THE PRICE OF

FREEDOM

By Simon Ivascu and Wesley Pop

Co-Author: **Bev Ellen Clarke**

3

Forewords

"Pas cu Pas." In the Romanian language "pas cu pas" means "step by step." This phrase is an apt description of how God guided and protected Simon and Wesley in their bold physical and spiritual journey from Romania to Canada.

In the pages of **The Price of Freedom** you will read a remarkable story of adventure, courage, mistakes and miracles. You'll thrill to see how in spite of incredible odds, God led these two young men to freedom. From fearful nights as escaping fugitives to long days as "cargo" on the high seas; from police prisons to "container" prisons, and from the status of illegal aliens to that of honorable citizens, this tale will reveal the power and love of God, and will grip you from first page to last.

But God led these two men to more than just political freedom! Along the convoluted path – pas cu pas – the promise of Proverbs 4:18 became theirs. They learned that indeed, "the path of the just is as the shining light, that shineth more and more unto the perfect day." In a few short years Simon and Wesley discovered more about God's love than many discover in a lifetime! Through mistakes, set-backs, and steel prisons opened with little more than their bare hands, these two young men discovered a God who never lets go and who gives hope and courage when life is at its darkest.

4

It has been our privilege to personally become well acquainted with Simon and Wesley. Their remarkable story and profound witness has inspired our lives and blessed our family. As you read this book it is our prayer you will discover a God who is intimately interested in your life. *The Price of Freedom* will strengthen your faith and we dare say, make you bolder in your "pas cu pas" – "step by step" journey!

Brad and Kandus Thorp
Hope Channel

Foreword

Throughout Biblical History, there have been men and women who, when faith was challenged, were determined to be faithful to their Creator God. Joseph faced prison rather than sin. Shadrach, Meshach, and Abednego experienced the fiery furnace rather than worship a false god. Many Christians were martyred for their faith because they could not blaspheme their God.

Such is also a story of two teenagers who determined to be true to their God no matter which obstacles stood in their way. They experienced extreme adversity, hardships and faced death just moments away, only to see the "light" of God saving them. The "Price of Freedom" is a story of miracles which brought Simon and Wesley to Canada, now their "home and native land."

A 'must read' book for young and old – a true modern-day miracle story.

Donald and Marilyn Melashenko

Simon and Wesley's story is first of all one of God's mercy and grace. Secondly it is one of two young men willing to sacrifice their lives rather than compromise their faith. Theirs is a story that will inspire you with a fresh picture of faith in a God that is still in control of a world gone mad. Simon and Wesley have dedicated their lives to honor their Lord who mercifully helped them in an impossible escape plan that become a reality. Today they sing praises to their great God and have dedicated their lives to bring hope to a world that is fast slipping into hopelessness. I have been blessed by their story of faith and their continued faithfulness to God.

Pastor Brian Hawes

Foreword

The disciples were tossed on a cold raging sea. But Jesus was sleeping so peacefully. They cried, "Master, Oh don't you care that we die?" He spoke three soft words, "Peace be still." It was the storm that had to die.

So don't be afraid when the darkness is closing. The Master is near His voice calms every storm. When the world says, "It's over" The Master says, "No. I've just begun!" In the darkest of times, whether rain or in sunshine, don't be afraid! I know how it feels to be tossed by the storm. I know how it feels to be battered and worn. Yet I know how it feels to be carried on thru. Calmed by the strength of the One, Who's been faithful and true.

So don't be afraid when the darkness is closing. The Master is near His voice calms every storm. When the world says, It's over" The Master says, "No. I've just begun!" In the darkest of times, whether rain or in sunshine, don't be afraid!*

*From "Don't Be Afraid." Words and music by Roger Bennett

Imagine, if you can, having hope for your future when you are a fugitive in your own country and are being beaten by the police in a foreign country. Imagine having hope for your future when you are spending sleepless nights on the run. Imagine having hope for your future when you are enduring long, miserable days trapped inside a cargo container that could very well be your tomb. Imagine having hope for your future when you are out of water, out of food, out of air...and out of time. Under these sorts of circumstances, sometimes it's hard to hold on to Gods faithfulness. But it's in times like these that we are reminded of this great promise found in Jeremiah 29:11. *"For I know the plans I have for you," declares the LORD, "plans to prosper you and not to harm you, plans to give you hope and a future." (NIV).* These are precisely the trials in which our faith is fortified.

The Bible defines faith as being *"sure of what we hope for and certain of what we do not see."* Simon and Wesley demonstrated just what it means to persevere with such a faith. They were sure for what they hoped. And what they hoped for was certainly something they could not see. But they pressed on in the face of extraordinary adversity, clinging to their hope in the Lord. Having lived in the United States all of my life, I have no concept of what life outside the comfort and security of American

7

democracy is like. I have never stood in a food line for hours hoping to get a ration of bread. I have never experienced the panic of breathing thru a straw to keep from suffocating, trapped inside a container ship bound for the shores of only God knows where. I have never been beaten and persecuted because I was a Christian. The closest most Americans come to these experiences is on television or at the local theater. But for Simon and Wesley, these were daily realities of life in the place where they called home. In this world, religious freedoms were nonexistent, meaning Christians like Simon and Wesley lived under the constant threat of harassment and punishment because of their faith.

Like so many Christians who have suffered for the sake of the cross, young Simon and Wesley faced a stark choice: Surrender in silence to the foes of their faith, or attempt a risky escape from the tyranny of communist Romania. And like so many believers before them, they found there really was no choice. Fleeing Romania might mean dying in the process, but staying would mean another kind of death-a slow spiritual death, being forced to hide in the light of the Savior and succumbing to religious persecution.

This book is the true story of two teenagers who left their homes and their families and risked their very lives for what every child of God deserves: Freedom to worship their creator. Though Simon and Wesley's circumstances were abysmal, their optimism is contagious, their attitude is infectious and their triumph is glorious! This book will be difficult to put down and its message of hope and the perseverance will remain with you, long after you've finished reading. Be prepared though. Thrust into this journey along side these brave young Christians, you'll often find yourself feeling nervous, scared, frustrated and even discouraged as Simon and Wesley's drama unfolds. But hold on my child...joy comes in the morning! More than just a captivating story, "The Price of Freedom" is a marvelous testimony to the faithfulness of these young men to their God...and the faithfulness of God to these young men.

Scott Fowler
Legacy Five

8

Table of Contents   Page

Table of Contents   Page

THE PRICE OF FREEDOM

A story of courage and faith in the face of danger...

A True Story

11

Chapter 1

Running Away From Home

The thin light of a late winter moon cast shadows over the furniture as Simon made his bed and took another quick look around his room. He knew it might be his last look; he might never see his home again.

Stepping carefully around the squeak in the floorboards, Simon stared again down the hallway to the other end of the house where his parents slept. His throat tightened. What if he never saw his parents again? It felt so wrong to leave with no good-bye.

His hands shook as once more he checked through his papers. The pride he felt about his new driver's license failed to bring a smile this time. Along with his passport and his other identification (ID), he tucked his license down into his left shirt pocket and buttoned it. The money he'd worked so hard to earn by selling his carved doors and wood creations looked insufficient against the enormity of what he was about to do. He stuffed the Hungarian money in one compartment and stashed the wad of German marks in the compartment with his Italian lire.

Simon's breath caught and held as a noise down the hallway halted his movements. Poised like a dark statue over his bed, Simon waited, listening. The noise didn't come again though, except for the sound of his own breathing, the house around him was silent. Simon didn't know what his parents would do if they awoke and saw him now in the act of leaving. Would his father be angry or disappointed in his youngest son? Would his mother cry or argue with him, and soften his heart to stay? Simon blinked rapidly to erase the stinging behind his eyelids and then he closed them, trying to think. It wasn't too late to back out of this plan. He could simply run out to the place where he was to meet his cousin, and tell him that he wouldn't need a ride to the border after all.

The bed still looked warm and inviting. His mother might make waffles when she woke up in a few hours. This was his home, after all. The little itch of excitement fueling his plans would soon fade in the reality of what lay ahead. Nothing about the new life he was imagining for himself could ever replace what he had right here with his family.

Simon's Family *(His oldest sister is not in the picture)*

Simon's eyes studied the moonlit shadows touching the wooden chest where he'd left his old guitar and all his hard–earned wood carving tools. They glided past his wooden artwork creations up on the wall along the notched wood top of the old bureau. And then they stopped at the picture of his brother, Stefan. But instead of seeing his smiling older brother in the photo, Simon saw Stefan the way he had looked the last time he had seen him. Stefan's ribs had been bandaged then. The bruises on his face were a darkened purple, and there had been a wild haunted look in Stefan's eyes.

Simon clenched his jaw as he tucked the wool scarf his eldest sister Lidia, had knit for him down into his leather jacket. He gathered in a slow deep breath to still his racing heart. There *was* no choice. If he didn't leave now, he would most likely suffer the same treatment that had almost killed his older brother.

There was no life for him here. He was short of breath and trembling with cold and anxiety when he slid into the cramped passenger seat of the little Opal hatchback.

"It's late," his cousin, Matthew, said. "I'm freezing here."

Simon glanced quickly back the way he'd come scanning for movement on the quiet streets. Then he met Matthew's eyes. "Sorry. It's hard to hurry when you are trying to stay quiet," he explained. He tried a brave grin that didn't seem to fit his mouth. "I guess I'm really doing this," he said.

Neither of them spoke as the car picked up speed and hurried along out of the village of "Moisei". What was there to say? Anything they spoke of would seem trivial at this point. Small talk could not dilute the intensity of Simon's dangerous path, and the effort of conversation would be a strain while Simon's mind reeled with matters of life and death.

After a few moments of driving Simon peeled off his gloves and rubbed his hands briskly in front of the barely warm heat vents. He pulled his packsack from the backseat where he'd stashed it just a few hours before and opened the top. Yes. His map of Hungary was there. Clothing, flashlight, food, music tapes, and Bible, it was all there, just the way he'd packed it. The cookies his mother had made just yesterday sat like a little bag of comfort, nestled in among his wool socks. Opening the bag now, he offered one to Matthew.

"Cookie?" he asked. "It's the raisin ones."

For a second Matthew looked as if he might take one. Then his eyes changed and he shook his head. "No thanks."

Simon put the cookies back into his packsack. He didn't think his stomach would even accept food right now. Settling back into the car seat he studied Matthew's profile as he navigated the dark road. Grateful for what his cousin was doing for him, Simon, in an attempt to express his thanks, asked, "Did you have any trouble leaving so early?"

Matthew shook his head. He glanced at Simon, worry narrowing his dark brows. "Another shooting was reported at this border," he said. "I just heard."

Simon tried to look nonchalant. Border shootings were not much of a shocker in Romania. He looked over at his cousin again when he felt Matthew's eyes go back to the road. Matthew was the only one who knew Simon's plan. He'd heard of Simon's intentions just this morning after church when Simon had asked for a ride to the border. Simon knew he could count on his cousin's silence.

Matthew understood why Simon was running. He'd survived his year of military service already and was glad to help Simon avoid the ordeal.

Every young man between the ages of eighteen and twenty knew from early childhood that they would be required to go into the army to give one year of their lives in military service. Stories of horrible army food, agonizing physical demands, harsh conditions and demanding officers were sometimes whispered among those of an age to get their orders. But it was the young men with strong Christian beliefs who faced the worst dangers in army life. Many gave up their faith in order to make it through their term of service. Those who clung to their beliefs, like Simon's brother, Stefan, were regularly ridiculed, mistreated and beaten, sometimes fatally. Stefan had landed in the army hospital after one of his beatings. While still recovering from his injuries, he had chosen to escape from Romania. He'd paid the dangerous price of freedom, risking prison and death, rather than return to his duties in the army.

Simon had been at home alone when Stefan stopped in to get some of his clothing before he left the country.

Simon had been so surprised to see his older brother that he hadn't said the things he'd wanted to. He'd been so distracted by the way his brother's hands shook as he rummaged through his clothing that his questions had been forgotten. Simon couldn't even remember what Stefan and him had talked about in those few moments, but he did recall the way Stefan's eyes had continually jumped around like a trapped animal.

Stefan

(Simon's brother)

Even now, years later, Simon didn't know much about what had happened to Stefan in the army. But he knew it had been bad. He knew he didn't want to face what Stefan had endured.

School had been bad enough sometimes, Simon thought. At public school he'd often faced mistreatment for being a Christian. But the physical and mental abuse Simon got from teachers when he was discovered slipping out of class before the weekends, or failing to attend on the weekends classes or tests, sounded rather lame in light of what he'd heard went on in the army.

Simon stuffed his fingers inside his jacket and watched the passing countryside, willing his mind to calmness. He knew they had to head northwest to get to the border, but he hadn't kept track of where they were or how far they had already come. They'd passed two villages already, or had it been three?

Just ahead on Simon's side a lone figure trudged between a darkened house and a barn. It looked to be a young man, heading out to possibly tend livestock. Simon watched the figure until they had passed the farm. It was early, not yet 4 am. Was this the usual time for morning chores or had this young man been unable to sleep because he had received his army orders? Simon sighed and closed his eyes remembering that his own army orders would come any time now. He knew few were eager to get the summons into the army, but there would not be many who would choose Simon's dangerous path to avoid the order.

He thought about some of his friends from school. Gustov, one of those who had sometimes ridiculed Simon for his beliefs, had received his orders several months ago, and he had spoken of it proudly. Gustov would never consider running from his army responsibility. He might even call Simon a coward for refusing his duty to serve his country.

Simon's Christian friends wouldn't find fault with the decision Simon was making though. Other young men in the church that Simon attended might even applaud Simon's bold strategy. Simon knew of some who had already fled the country and others who would probably try to escape rather than risk losing their faith or facing the severe persecution army life would bring.

Simon thought, even Vasile (Wesley) a friend of his, might try to leave. He knew that Wesley might be the type who would take a chance to escape Romania if he could. Wesley lived in Viseu De Jos, a village a fair distance from where Simon grew up, but Simon had often heard Wesley sing at big church gatherings. He'd sung with Wesley once at a country–wide evangelistic service when he'd been only thirteen. The memory felt clear even now after more than five years; the stage and the lights, Wesley's easy grin. Simon felt proud singing in front of so many people with his friend. Wesley had his own band and he was known by everyone in the area as a singer.

Simon at age 14   *Wesley at age 13*

Being the same age as Simon, Wesley could be facing an army decision right now, too, and Simon didn't think Wesley would be the type who would give up his faith or go quietly into army service.

As the car was finally getting warm, Simon kept his eyes closed. He knew it would be good for him to get some sleep, but rest felt a long way off. His heart would not stop racing. To calm his breathing, slow his heartbeat, and stop his head from going around and around over his worries and plans, Simon tried to pray. Unbidden, the words of a song drifted into his mind "A song we sing, a song like no other . . . I'll not be afraid, I can trust that He will see me through." He and Wesley had sung this song together so many years ago. When he'd sung it then, it hadn't held much meaning for him, but now the words seemed like the words of a prayer, a prayer he needed now. As the miles sped by, Simon let the words repeat in his mind, and he pondered his faith. He'd never doubted the truth of his beliefs, but he wondered, now, if God *would* help him. Would God "see him through" as the words of the song said? Did the Almighty Creator God really care about one insignificant person with some rather desperate plans? Did He approve of Simon's actions? Simon didn't know if he even expected his heavenly Father to intervene to protect him. He didn't know if he really believed that God would help him get safely through the dangers ahead. Faith suddenly felt like a fragile thing he had never completely grasped. He grabbed out for it, clutching for it with the words of the song. "A song we sing, a song like no other...*Because He Lives*."

They'd been driving for almost three hours, and the night sky had begun to lighten when Simon noticed that Matthew had begun to look apprehensive. They had climbed a bit higher into country that looked somewhat more desolate and Simon scanned the area watching for whatever seemed to have alerted his cousin. There was little to see. Fields mostly, and scrub brush. Spring still felt far away in these parts, and there were bigger patches of snow than back in *Moisei*, and in the distance a thick forest darkened the landscape.

Simon felt his heart jump when he squinted towards the woods. Was that dark shape a wolf? He'd always feared wolves because wolf stories had been the scariest ones for him, and this country looked like a place wolves might live. He looked back at Matthew to ask if he had seen a movement when his cousin began slowing the car.

"Here?" Simon asked. His voice squeaked with the question.

"I think the border is fairly close," Matthew replied. He sounded uncertain. Afraid maybe. "I don't want to be spotted," he added. The car had stopped, but Matthew was already looking back, cramping the wheels over to turn the little car around.

Simon nodded. He knew his cousin could get in a lot of trouble just for being close to the border, and he was grateful for Matthew's help.

But the words he wanted to say to him seemed to stick in his throat while the warmth and safety of the car rendered him unable to make a move.

"I'd head into the woods, there, if I were you," Matthew said, pointing.

Reluctantly Simon turned his head toward the dark trees across the field. One hand reached up to check that his ID was still safely in his left pocket even though there would be no way it could have moved since he'd put it there. His other hand reached down for his packsack. When he managed to reach out for the door handle his fingers trembled. This was it. When he got out of this car there would be no more chances to turn back or change his mind.

He managed to speak his words of thanks before he said good–bye, but he didn't look back to see if Matthew waved when he drove away. He was running by that time, for it would be dangerous to be seen close to the border and easy to spot out there in the open.

In the cover of the trees, the quiet stillness felt instantly safer but somehow smothering. The colorless early dawn looked bleak, and grey light filtered through the shades of brown surrounding him. The only movement came from the steam pushing out around Simon's face as he struggled to catch his breath.

He was alone.

Running kept him warm. He stayed in the forest, with one eye on the road for direction. The border wasn't as close as Matthew had believed, but he came to it finally without any difficulty. It wasn't hard to miss.

Simon sucked in a breath and backed farther into the trees to study the layout. Near the road to the border, crossing a tall fence marked the boundary. A look out tower watched the world from high in the air. Uniformed guards paced along the border's perimeter, and a wide swath of tilled ground lay in wait to expose the footprints of anyone who dared to cross the boundary off road.

Simon slumped forward into the tree that sheltered him as thoughts of hunger evaporated with one glimpse of what lay ahead.

After an hour of watching the guards' movements, Simon found a well concealed hiding spot where he could see the whole border crossing. And there he watched.

Simon watched through the entire day deciding that he needed the cover of darkness. Night would be his only hope of crossing unseen, but the hours of light ahead of him stretched out interminably. He hadn't slept all night, but neither could he relax enough to even feel sleepy. He turned up the collar of his leather coat and tucked his hands under his arms against the cold February morning.

Even after he'd learned the schedule of which guards walked in which direction and at what hours, he couldn't relax. He ticked off the hours by timing every movement of the guards, memorizing their positions and studying the route he would run. And then he waited, and he watched some more. He ate most of the cookies and thought fondly of his mother. He closed his eyes and brought back the smell of the kitchen when she was baking, and the way she smiled at his jokes. The cold had seeped through his clothing and flesh, all the way into his bones by the time daylight faded. He had to rub his fingers and hands frequently to generate some warmth.

While he waited out the fading light, Simon had time to think about death. He clamped his jaw tight and felt his teeth press against each other painfully as he imagined how a bullet might feel, slamming into his back. The guards on duty at the border crossings would not hesitate to shoot.

They would yell a warning, "Halt," only once before they fired. Even in the dark their aim would likely be fatal. And if they didn't see him running but spotted his footprints in the turned soil, they would quickly alert the Hungarian border to be on the lookout for him. He wouldn't be safe until he had crossed the kilometer of neutral land between the two borders and then passed over the Hungarian border somewhere up ahead in the darkness.

Simon didn't make his move until well past the fall of darkness. He couldn't see his watch and it was too risky to turn on his flashlight for even a moment, but he guessed by the size and location of the almost full moon that it was after midnight.

He worked out the painful cramps in his leg muscles, tried to tempt some warm blood into his arms and fingers with some vigorous arm flapping, and then stood straight to suck down great gulps of air as he prepared to run.

Chapter 2

Crossing Borders

Simon had always been a fast runner. His long legs were strong and quick in school races and soccer but they betrayed him now. In the soft plowed earth they seemed to be moving no faster than a walk. It felt as if he were trapped once more in one of his childhood nightmares, moving in slow motion as some faceless enemy grew closer and closer.

The moon played tricks on him, squeezing out from behind its warm nest of clouds to get a better look at Simon's desperate flight. It outlined his shadow and cast his footprints into dark relief.

The field seemed to extend longer ahead of him as he ran. When he stumbled, the cold spongy soil grabbed at his arms and hands as he fell. The plunge startled a yelp out of his throat, past his labored breathing, and he bit his lip against the sound to search around once more for any movement.

"God, please hide me . . ." he breathed. "Don't let them see me. Please . . ."

Was God listening? Simon couldn't tell. Terror weighed him down, like a ball of ice low in his gut.

He fell onto his belly as soon as he saw the Hungarian side of the border. He was hidden behind a hillock, but he felt exposed in the moonlit night. His breath came out ragged as if he had run a marathon, but he knew it was only a kilometer between the two boundaries.

Simon couldn't afford to watch long this time for it wasn't safe to linger here. Even now the guards at the Romanian border could have spotted his footprints and called ahead to the Hungarian patrol guards. With every ounce of his focus Simon concentrated on measuring the intervals of time between guards patrolling the Hungarian border. His body heat had barely drained into the cold earth beneath him, and his breathing had scarcely slowed before he was on his feet once more, running.

He didn't stop until he was well past the border and the road. He was in Hungary now safely out of Romania, but not out of danger. He had no travel visa; he'd left the country illegally. If he were caught here, or reported, he'd face far more trouble than being sent into army service.

After awhile, exhaustion forced his legs into a walk, but Simon didn't stop to rest. He gulped water from his water bottle and continued walking as dawn lightened the sky.

Under the cover of trees that looked reassuringly like the Romanian trees he had crept through the night before, Simon felt hidden. However with so much forest, and a real danger of losing all sense of direction and becoming hopelessly lost, Simon paid careful attention to landmarks around him. Several times he stopped for a moment where the trees let in a patch of light so he could consult his little compass and squint up at the sun.

It was full daylight under thick white cloud when Simon finally felt the forest fading into fields and flatter land. He stopped to eat some canned fish, and when he found a road at last he boldly decided to walk along it.

He was a fugitive. He knew if he were stopped or questioned, his escape would be over, but he would get nowhere hiding all day. He needed to find a train station, and it would be more easily found if he followed the roads

With little traffic at first, Simon waved congenially to a man who passed him walking in the other direction. Then he caught up with and passed two women walking in his direction who both smiled at him shyly. For all they knew he was just a farm lad heading into town. He could pass easily enough as Hungarian if he remembered to keep his mouth shut, and if no one decided to speak to him or ask him anything he'd be okay.

The map he'd folded up to carry in his jacket pocket helped some as he struggled to sort out directions. He could compare roadside place names with village names on his map, but with no knowledge of the Hungarian language he couldn't ask for directions to the train station or read anything of what was written on signs along the road.

Simon had been on his feet running or walking for over eight hours when he came to a village and found a train station. From his own map and the one posted near the ticket office, Simon located a town close to the border of Austria. Then with his heart beating in his throat, he paid for a newspaper and then a train ticket mostly by pointing and smiling.

After that he tried to convince his face and body to relax. He knew if he looked at all suspicious, the train conductor would ask questions and demand to see his ID and passport. Even if he didn't look suspicious, there was a chance that this would be where it all ended if the train conductor took any interest in him at all.

Simon pretended to be engrossed in reading the newspaper he had purchased as soon as he'd selected a seat. He hoped that having his head buried in a newspaper would save him from having to speak to anyone.

"Tickets!" the train conductor shouted. Then once again, louder, he shouted over the noise of the now moving train. "Tickets!"

As the train conductor moved through the car collecting tickets, Simon stared at the undecipherable printing on one page of his newspaper. With a casualness contradicting the turmoil in his nervous stomach, and without making eye contact with the conductor, Simon positioned his body carelessly over the double vinyl covered train seat he had chosen and held up his ticket. He kept his head down, as if engrossed in an interesting article and remembered to breathe again only after the conductor had snatched the ticket from his hand and moved on.

After walking without rest for so long, the chance to sit awhile felt good. The train vibrated soothingly beneath him and the hum of the engine and the tracks was almost hypnotic, but Simon couldn't sleep. His mind wouldn't rest for he was fearful of missing his stop. He watched the land rush by out his window, a blur of buildings, fields, and villages. Planting had not yet begun and the countryside showed little green or sign of spring. Fields were brown and bare, trees leafless, and the villages they stopped at or sped through looked grey in the cloudy afternoon.

Across from him an elderly man that resembled Simon's grandfather risked a smile in Simon's direction. Simon smiled back hesitantly and then blinked furiously at his newspaper. He was tired enough to cry, and if he thought about his grandfather he might have to cry knowing that he would probably never see his grandfather again.

Gloom caught up to him. Here on the train, surrounded by people speaking a language he couldn't understand, Simon felt more alone than he had in the forest. He was cut off. He'd left his home, his family and friends, and his country; this was harder than he had expected. He'd been on the run for almost 24 hours, but no one would be worrying yet, except perhaps his cousin, Matthew, who knew what he had done. Simon's parents would probably think their youngest son had gone into the city to take some more orders for the wooden doors he carved. Likely they wouldn't even start to wonder about him for days yet. Somehow that thought made him feel even lonelier. It was as if he could somehow disappear more easily if no one knew where he was. If none who cared about him knew where he was or what he was attempting, perhaps he could just vanish forever. No one would even know what had happened to him.

God knew, of course. Was He watching over Simon now? Was God's close watch the reason he had made it this far? Simon wanted to believe it was true, but it was still hard to convince himself that God, with a universe to oversee, could take a personal interest in Simon's troubles.

To avoid any suspicion, Simon got off the train some distance from the Austrian border. There were at least two more towns before the edge of Hungary according to his map, and once off the train it felt like too great a distance to hike. He was weary from two days and two nights without sleep, and he still had Hungarian money left so he hired a taxi. With gestures and grunts and some pointing at his map, Simon was able to instruct the scruffy looking driver where to take him. It was a village as close as he dared to get to the border. In spite of riding the train and then a taxi, it was still quite late on Monday night when Simon got to the Hungarian border crossing. It had taken a full day to cross the country.

Simon's plan was to cross the border that night. He'd wait for darkness when the moon was hidden by clouds, if possible. Then he would run. He'd successfully crossed through two patrolled borders now, and he felt more confident of what to expect.

At the first sight of the border, however, his confidence melted like frost at noonday. The patrols at this border crossing walked with huge scent trained guard dogs. They seemed to be making their rounds quite frequently, too.

Afraid of letting the dogs catch his scent, Simon climbed into a tree to wait. He ate some bread, opened a tin of meat and devoured two small apples as he stared across the short distance to where clouds of steam surrounded the open mouths of the guard dogs. He let his imagination picture the horror of being run down by a huge dog. They looked a bit like wolves at this distance and he wondered what they would do when they were let off leash to run him down. Would they bite into his legs as he fell, grab hold and shake, or would they stand on top of him with a death hold on his neck as they waited for the guards to arrive?

As Simon watched the activity at the border, cold air worked its way inside him once more, and fear turned the contents of his hasty dinner uncomfortably around and around in his stomach.

But he fell asleep anyway.

He woke up surprised. It was the first time he had slept since he had left home. But tired as he was, he hadn't thought he would be able to sleep in such a precarious spot. This scared him a little, and he doubled his efforts to stay alert. He dozed in snatches once or twice more during the night hours, but he was never completely relaxed. Even while asleep he felt as if one eye was always open, watching.

In the darkest hours of the night uneasiness held him with cold, clutching hands. What he attempted here was folly. Even if he wasn't killed outright, his life would be over if he was caught now. Prison would be next for him, and he would be locked up for a long time for trying to evade military duty. If he survived his time in jail, he would still be forced to serve time in the army. He didn't know if he could afford this high price for his freedom. He'd been too cocky planning this escape. What had he been thinking? Had he really thought through the risk while he'd been dreaming up this foolhardy plan? Was his *life* to be the price of his freedom?

All day Tuesday, Simon worried. He stayed up in his tree, doing surveillance mostly. He learned the routine of the patrol guards and their dogs, timing out their changes, the route they followed walking, and the amount of time everyone took with each go round. And he waited. His muscles cramped and his fingers and

toes ached with a numbing cold, but the strength of his
him from moving until darkness had settled solidly down
the trees around him, and he had timed out a wi
opportunity in the middle of a patrol round.

Once more Simon crossed a border running for his life,
dreading to hear someone shout out an alarm or command,
"Halt!" He passed through the Hungarian border and raced over
the plowed no man's land towards Austria. But there were no trees
for cover here and nowhere to hide. Around the tall guard towers
of the Austrian border were only open fields.

Simon flattened himself in a sort of ditch frantically
scanning for the guards. Waiting wasn't an option he could afford
here, so, with his eyes glued to the tower look outs, Simon crept
across another border, crossing the boundary into Austria
practically within touching distance of the posts holding up the
look out towers.

He walked through the dark of the night, longing for
daylight, but fearing it, too, for almost immediately, Austria felt
different from Hungary or Romania. Cars looked newer, and more
plentiful and seemed to be going faster. There were parks and
landscaped areas. Roadsides looked tidier, houses and yards well
kept and more affluent. He caught a glimpse of well-dressed
people. In his dirty rumpled clothing Simon suddenly felt
conspicuous. Looking as he did, he didn't think he could
intermingle as easily anymore in this new place for he needed a
bath, clean clothing and a shave.

To keep from being seen or arousing suspicion, he walked
in the trees, in the shadows of buildings, and behind bushes and
vehicles. Whenever he could, he kept the roads in view to guide
him.

He knew family friends who lived close to Vienna. His
father's good friend, Eugin had come to Austria several years ago.
Simon's hope was to contact him for help. And that meant he had
to risk entering a town and finding a train station again.

He found a phone and called the number he'd been given by his brother's friend. It was the phone number of a Romanian man named Malik, who helped people like Simon with transportation and border crossings.

It was the middle of the night still, but Malik answered his phone as if he had been wide awake. He instructed Simon where to wait and then arrived promptly but looking wary. Sizing up Simon's appearance with a glance, he made a quick motion with the large well-muscled arm hanging out the window and growled, "Get in."

The amount of money Malik asked for seemed high to Simon but there was no negotiating as he was in no position to barter. He was an illegal immigrant now; here in a foreign country without permission, without a travel visa and without a way to communicate with the people or even read the signs to travel safely. As he counted out the German marks Malik had asked for, Simon told himself that the service Malik was providing was well worth the cost. This man with the shifty eyes and quick movements would take him safely through Vienna and get him to Ternitz to the home of his friend. In Eugin's home he would finally feel safe enough to sleep in a real bed, maybe. He could clear his mind and maybe even get some help for the next stages of his journey. He could finally wash, change his clothes and eat a hot meal. The way he felt right now, Simon thought he might gladly part with every cent he carried for such luxuries.

Malik wasn't much for chit chat, but Simon did learn that his new chauffeur had already been detained once and had been suspected of aiding illegal immigrants at another time. Malik told Simon, "I can't afford to take any chances. Are you listening to me? To help you is very dangerous to me."

There was not much Simon could say to that. He thanked Malik, nodded politely, and watched out his window as Austria sped past him.

Simon estimated that they had been driving for about two hours when they first started seeing the outskirts of Vienna. Even in the still dark of the early morning Simon could see the vastness of this city and appreciate that he had Malik to take him where he needed to go.

And then, without warning, Malik slowed his car and slammed one hand down repeatedly on the steering wheel.

"What?" Simon asked. He sat up straight to look.

Malik cursed and swept a powerful arm out quickly against Simon's chest. "Get down. Down on the floor," he ordered. "It's a road block. The police." The big man cursed once more and Simon could see his dark eyes jumping anxiously in every direction. "They will ask for papers. You have to get out of my car," he told Simon.

Simon stared at Malik over his crunched up knees where he had folded himself onto the floor of the car. "No . . . ," he began as his hand came up automatically to feel his ID papers still safely inside his pocket.

Malik glared down at him. "I told you. I can't afford to be caught now with someone like you. I'll be deported. Worse!" Malik's eyes stared ahead now, and both of his hands rested on the steering wheel with his arms straight in front of him. "I'm going to run it," he told Simon. "We're going to crash straight through, and then you will get out." His tone implied that there would be no discussion. "There's some change on the dash here. You can use it to make a telephone call. You can grab that when you go. But you must get out. I won't have you in my car."

Simon bit down on his lip; he turned his head and searched for the door handle as Malik put his foot to the gas pedal.

The car sped ahead and then stopped to turn sharply. Gravel spun as the tires slid.

"Now!" Malik shouted at him. "Go!"

The car was still rolling, swerving, but Simon pushed the door open and jumped. Malik had fixed it so no light would come on as the door opened, and he had positioned his car so that it was between Simon and the police road block.

Simon rolled onto the uneven pavement and hit the ground moving. One fist still clutched a handful of change, the other clung to his packsack. His knee stung where he'd landed on the hard road. His eyes searched frantically for somewhere to hide. Even though it was still dark he knew the police would be on their way here. They would suspect that Malik had been drinking or that he had something to hide after a crazy stunt of charging through a police barricade.

A parked tractor trailer provided instant cover for Simon. He dashed behind a tire that stood as tall as his shoulder and tried to fade into shadow. Had they seen him? Slowly he bent his sore knee to crouch beside the tire trying to get a look at the road. The deafening sound of his own heartbeat made it hard to hear anything, but there were people moving. Gravel crunched as someone came closer.

What could he do? Simon clenched his jaw and stifled a groan that almost escaped from his throat. If the police discovered him here the days and nights of no sleep, the border terror, the running, everything . . . It would all have been for nothing. Everyone knew about the strict laws in Austria.

There were voices now, but another set of footsteps.

Slowly, so as to make no noise, Simon twisted to move under the truck trailer. He felt along underneath the rig and crawled silently up on top of the back axle, holding his breath as clods of dirt fell onto the ground.

Two sets of black police boots were right beside the truck now. One pair stood still and the other moved around the truck. The set of boots that had stopped moving suddenly burst into light as a flashlight came on and swept back and forth along the tires of the rig.

The moving pair of boots stopped close to where Simon had stood hiding a moment ago. And then Simon could see the policeman's head peering under the trailer.

Chapter 3

Hiding in Austria

It took a few moments for Simon to relax his tensed muscles and feel his breathing return to normal after the policemen left the truck and walked back to the road block. He closed his eyes.

"*God, you must be watching over me,*" he whispered. "*Thank you. Thank you, God. Please don't let anyone come to drive this truck away.*" He squirmed around, working his body into an easier position. And then, once more, he waited. Although just as cold and uncomfortable, unlike the tree he had waited in hours ago, this spot offered no view. It was maddening to hear noises and voices and not be able to see what was happening.

An occasional sound confirmed that the police were still stopping cars, but Simon hadn't heard Malik's voice. He didn't know what had become of the Romanian who had helped him get this far until he heard what sounded a bit like Malik's car starting.

And even then he didn't know if it had been Malik leaving or someone else driving his car away.

For another two hours Simon lay on top of the truck axle, afraid to move. Dawn had begun to color a new day by the time the police all drove away.

Simon ached all over when he crept out from his hiding spot around 5 am. His nerves were so on edge that he yelped in alarm when he caught a glimpse of his image in the truck side mirror. His face was dirty, his dark curly hair looked grey with powdery dust, and he hardly recognized the dark eyes that stared back at him.

With the pack slung over his shoulder Simon looked like a ragged vagrant. He would be picked up or pointed out as soon as a police or any patriotic citizen caught sight of him. With a heavy sigh Simon crouched down in the shadow of the truck wheel once more and opened his packsack. He took out his Bible and stuffed it into his pocket. Then he ruffled through his maps, papers and pictures and selected one or two he could not part with. For several long moments he stared at all his precious music cassette tapes, his clothing, and the other belongings he had so carefully selected to take with him. His mother had sewn this packsack for him, and he hated to leave any of it behind. To discard such dear possessions felt like abandoning part of his body. How could he just leave it sitting here on the side of the road, as if he were discarding unimportant junk?

But it had to be done.

The way he looked as he traveled with a packsack, he might as well shout aloud that he was a fugitive, here illegally, on the run. He had to leave it behind.

Simon veered off the highway where the police had been as soon as a lesser road presented itself. He moved behind parked cars, swerved off to walk dark alleys between buildings and crept through road construction equipment warily, looking around constantly. It would be light soon, and much easier to be spotted. He had no map of Vienna and no sense of which direction to take to get to Ternitz, so once more he hoped to find the train station. The train, when he finally did hear it though, sounded a long way away. The way the town was laid out it looked impossible to even get to the tracks to follow them to the station.

When he spotted the public phone Simon decided that he would phone Eugin. Ternitz wasn't too far from Vienna so perhaps he could ask his father's old friend to come and pick him up here.

Using the coins that he had grabbed in Malik's car, Simon dialed the number. It was the right number, but Eugin was not at home.

The man who answered identified himself as Eugin's brother, Jon, and told him, "He's not home yet. He works the night shift."

So Simon waited once more. Patience was becoming a skill.

Eugin answered the phone the next time Simon called. "I am Simon Ivascu, Stefan's son, from Romania. Do you remember Stefan Ivascu Sr.?" he asked Eugin. "I am here now. In Vienna." He waited for Eugin's response anxiously. Then he added, "I need your help. If you could come and pick me up . . . "

"Where are you?" Eugin asked.

"Vienna," Simon answered.

A hoarse chuckle sounded on the other end. "Vienna is a big place," Eugin said. His voice sounded familiar now and Simon pressed the phone tighter against his ear to better catch the friendly sounding words. He remembered in a flash an image of Eugin and his father leaning over some car of Eugin's in their driveway. While his father had been helping to fix something the car slipped out of gear and rolled, stopping with a crash against the brick wall of the garage, Eugin laughed. Simon had been a boy then, quite young but he recalled Eugin's hoarse sounding voice and the big cheerful sound of his laughter.

Eugin's voice interrupted Simon's thoughts. "How will I find you?" he asked.

Quickly Simon tried to describe his surroundings. But even as he spoke he realized that his description would likely fit many places in a large city. He looked farther, searching for some kind of distinguishing signs or indications to mark where he was. How could he ask for help for someone to rescue him if he didn't even know where he was? "I don't know," he told Eugin. "Hold on. I will look for a street sign." But there were no street signs anywhere close. Simon ran back to the phone. "I can't find a street sign," he panted. He watched the phone counting down his time. The change he had used up on this last call was running out.

"So how will you get to us?" Eugin asked.

"I don't know," Simon repeated. He had no more coins to add. He pressed the phone against his ear, hoping that Eugin would have an answer hoping for a miracle. But no miracle came. Instead, the connection clicked out, and a dial tone sounded in his ear. Time had run out.

Simon hung up the phone and stared unable to believe a voice that had sounded so amiable and so willing to help could vanish so cruelly.

He had Eugin's address, but he would have to ask for help to find the way there. And he could not speak German. His obvious inability to speak the language, and his disheveled appearance would arouse suspicion immediately if he approached anyone on the street for help.

His thoughts had grown slow and disordered. He was so tired, but he needed to think and plan. A taxi, he decided, after a few moments. A taxi would be risky, but it might be his only hope.

Simon made his way to a busier street to find a taxi. And when he finally did see what he thought might be a taxi, he boldly stood in the road to wave it down. Dread crept inside of him as it approached. He realized he might actually be flagging down a police vehicle. The round dome light on the car heading towards him was common on taxis and police cars. From a distance it was impossible to tell.

When he was sure the vehicle was indeed a taxi, Simon strolled to the driver's window. To the balding man with the brooding expression behind the wheel, Simon tried to give the impression that he was from Italy. Italians had greater freedom of travel than Romanians, and Simon knew it would be safer to appear to be a lost foreigner from Italy than a young man from Romania. He knew a few words in Italian, and he used them now, gesturing to the paper with Eugin's address. He put on a friendly grin and acted out the part of a carefree traveler.

The stern faced driver didn't return Simon's smile. With growing anxiety, Simon watched as the driver looked him over, stared down at the address in Simon's hand and then turned off the meter, and the light on top of the cab. The man picked up his dispatch car radio next and began speaking in German.

The hair on the back of Simon's neck prickled upright. Was the man already reporting Simon to the authorities? Should Simon run? Or would running be worse?

"*How much?*" Simon asked bravely, in Italian. He pointed at the meter.

The taxi driver held up three fingers. "Deutch mark."

"*Marks? Three hundred mark?*"

The driver grunted and pointed. He seemed to be trying to explain how far it was to the address where Simon wished to go.

Simon shrugged and paid the man. It was a lot of money too much probably, but he began to think that perhaps the frowning man was more interested in making money than in turning him in. He had probably identified Simon as illegal, but had turned off his meter and his dispatch not in order to call the police but to make a bit of profit for himself on the side. Simon decided that paying a high price for a taxi ride was better than being driven to the authorities.

Even after paying his money and settling into the car, Simon did not feel safe. If the man regularly turned off his meter to make more money for himself he was probably not a trustworthy type. He could collect Simon's money and still turn him in. But in spite of tension in every part of his body, Simon could not keep his eyes open as the taxi drove through the city. His head slumped down, and he slept for almost an hour. They had

39

crossed through Vienna when Simon realized the car had stopped moving. With a start of panic, Simon jolted full awake. *I am at the police station*, he thought.

He gazed at his watch in disbelief and then looked around him wondering if there was enough time to make an escape, to bolt out of this trap. But there was nothing that resembled a police station. No police cars. The driver was again speaking words he didn't understand. He pointed at the address and then at a map and threw up his hands at the area around them.

Confused still, Simon slowly grasped that in spite of having Eugin's address in front of him, the taxi driver apparently could not find the place. And then Simon noticed that the car was stopped beside another public phone. With a coin borrowed from the driver, Simon phoned Eugin once more. This time when Eugin asked where Simon was, Simon put the taxi driver on the phone.

The taxi driver was speaking German and Simon could hear German words coming through the phone as well. They were apparently close to where Eugin lived, but Eugin instructed him to wait there, and he would come meet him. Fear was in Eugin's words. He sounded guarded perhaps afraid of letting the taxi driver come to his home and identify a place that would house a fugitive.

When Eugin arrived he and Simon stood together on the road stealing cautious looks at each other. Eugin's face looked different, Simon thought. Perhaps it was his beard. And he seemed older, shorter than Simon had remembered him. But Simon had grown tall in the few years since his father's friend had left Romania.

"Your father is well?" Eugin asked.

Simon nodded.

Eugin grunted. "A good man, your father." Once more the older man studied Simon's face. He seemed to be trying to make up his mind about something. Then unexpectedly he pointed and began walking, leading the way to where he had left his parked car.

40

It was Friday morning, almost a full week since Simon had left his home in Romania. He had arrived with only the clothing on his back and a bit of money in his pocket, and it had been almost a full week since he had taken a shower or eaten a real meal or slept lying down. He almost wept with gratitude when he finally was offered these comforts. It wasn't safe for him to go anywhere in Austria, but inside the apartment, he could relax at last.

In the morning when Eugin and Jon went to church, Simon stayed behind in the apartment. He wanted to attend; he needed the familiarity of the worship service and fellow believers after his harrowing week. He'd rarely missed attending church for any reason and it felt wrong to miss going, but Simon could not risk being seen, or having anyone ask questions, and so he stayed inside the apartment for almost three weeks.

Eugin had been in Austria for several years, but had still not received his permanent status. Once over his initial guarded reception he welcomed Simon with a genuine hospitality, and he and his brother, Jon, willingly shared their food and the small apartment where they lived. Neither would consider Simon's request for a ride to the Italian border, however. Such a trip would be too dangerous.

"I must be careful, my friend," Eugin told Simon. "Just to have you here I take a chance, you know. I am close to becoming a citizen, but my record must be very clean to receive my papers. Austria, you know, have many rules here, and I cannot take a risk."

Simon did understand. "I know," he assured Eugin. "You have already done too much. I would not want to put you in jeopardy of being deported after working so hard these past years. I will find another way."

But there did not seem to be another way. No one was willing to drive Simon to the Italian border for everyone was afraid. It was not the type of service Simon could ask of just anyone without peril to his own safety. As the days passed, Simon grew restless and impatient. Waiting grew almost intolerable, but his fears of being caught did not diminish. He hid, frightened as a rabbit in a burrow when the mailman came to the door. A vehicle stopping near the apartment jarred his heart into a new rhythm. Even Eugin or Jon returning home, making a noise at the door before they entered, would often cause Simon alarm.

When Eugin suggested that Simon might be able to help with a roofing job, he did not hesitate to agree. He'd been cooped up in the apartment too long and he was eager to repay Eugin and Jon for their generosity. Besides, the work was an easy task of removing shingles on a home in a field out of the city somewhere. Simon welcomed the opportunity to help and to be outside.

Eugin's brother–in–law, Edgar, gave Simon a ride to the work place. Even that task Eugin would not risk doing himself.

"I have only a visitor visa myself," Edgar told Simon. He grinned at Simon's anxious face as the two of them folded their equally tall frames into his little Volkswagen Rabbit. Then he shrugged and laughed. "Don't worry."

The day had turned out warm, bright with possibilities, and Edgar's unruffled attitude was infectious. Simon rearranged his passenger seat so that his knees didn't bump the front dash and began to relax. *After all, what could happen*, he asked himself? Simon was not some unwashed vagabond scurrying along behind parked cars like some scared–looking stray cat today. He was a guy going off to a job like every other person did in Ternitz. He was shaved, showered and wearing clean clothes, riding in a car. What could happen?

Almost as he thought of it, though, the unthinkable did happen.

Edgar was pulled over by the police for speeding!

As the two policemen walked towards the car and then began looking through the windows of the small vehicle peering into the back seat and at Simon, the easy going smile slipped from Edgar's face. A pale mask had transformed his friendly countenance into an expression of fear that Simon recognized. He'd seen that fear on Romanian faces too many times. Edgar's calloused hands shook and fumbled as he found his ID and handed his visitor visa to the police at his driver's side window.

Simon knew that it would be his turn next. It was common practice for authorities to ask for the passenger's ID as well as the driver's. Simon felt his hand go up to his shirt pocket where he'd buttoned in his ID as usual this morning. It wouldn't do him any good, of course. When the police saw his identification he would be arrested instantly. Just one look at Simon's age and citizenship on his Romanian driver's license by these policemen would put an end to Simon's dreams of joining his brother in Italy.

Simon willed his body to something less tense. *"Calm down,"* he told himself. Look natural. Smile. Breathe. He couldn't seem to keep air flowing into his lungs. The small car suddenly felt like a prison, and he was trapped.

While the officer on Edgar's side of the car frowned at Edgar's identification, Simon shifted his feet, feeling his toes tighten and release inside the work boots Jon had lent to him. What would he say when they turned their attention to question him?

But the question didn't come. The police wrote out a speeding ticket for Edgar and then walked back to their car and pulled away. Relief and gratitude washed through Simon like a drink of water after a long thirst.

Edgar let out something between a snort and a chuckle. "That was too close," he said. He started laughing. Beside him, Simon closed his eyes. Then he joined in the laughter, letting the tension ease out of his body.

The incident had shaken them both, and they spent some time planning a route of escape for Simon once they reached the job site. If the police came, as they often did, to check up on construction sites where illegal immigrants were likely to find work, Simon was to scramble to the low point of the roof where they were working and jump down near the back porch into a neighbor's back yard.

It wasn't until a bit later, when he glanced at his route of escape, that Simon noticed the large, mean—looking dog in the yard he would have to traverse. He desperately hoped he would not have to jump down there beside such a brute.

In spite of the fact that working outside felt good after being cooped up in the apartment so long, Simon was on edge most of the day. He was glad to finally get back to the apartment.

When he related the day's events to Jon, Eugin stood shaking his head. He let out his breath in one long whistle and then fixed serious eyes on Simon's face. "No more going out of this place," he said to Simon. His hands made a cutting off motion as he shook his head once more. "No more. It's not worth it. That was too close." Once more he shook his head. "You stay here from now on, yes?"

Simon was only too willing to agree. But once again the days stretched long. Simon paced the floor of the small rooms and tried to plot his future. On that day, he watched his friends dress for church and leave to worship without him.

Jon sensed Simon's discontent. To distract him from his thoughts he spoke with Simon about his truck. Simon had some mechanical knowledge and Jon needed advice about his truck's engine problems. He needed his vehicle for work, but the truck's problems had been growing more severe and Jon didn't have enough money to take it to a mechanic.

"I think I could help you fix that," Simon told Jon. "It sounds like a clutch problem." He told Jon what tools would be needed and what adjustments might be necessary.

"We'll get the truck hauled out to Durik's farm," Jon suggested to Eugin. "He's way up there in the mountains. The police would never come there."

Eugin frowned.

"One morning is all it would take," Simon persuaded. He wanted to do this thing. There was little enough he could do that would repay the brothers for aiding him.

When the day dawned clear and warm, Simon was glad Eugin had agreed. The air felt cool and fresh in the mountains. As they drove, Simon glanced many times in the direction he needed to go to reach the Italian border. The high rugged ridge of mountains was much different than the rolling hills he'd navigated through Romania and Hungary. He measured the height of the mountains with his determination, and in spite of the spring scented wind and the blue sky, he felt a tremor gnaw at the edges of his courage.

At the sheep farm Simon stayed alert to every sound. Jon had towed his truck into the farmyard where Simon could work unseen from the road. He was surrounded by barns and fences and sheep enclosures, but he stood up quickly from his task each time he heard a vehicle that sounded as if it were entering the driveway.

He'd been working on the truck alone for several hours when he stood up to the sound of a car coming down the driveway. He could hardly believe his eyes when he noticed the dome on the top of the vehicle and the familiar police colors. A police car!

At first his mind didn't register what he was seeing. Hadn't Jon told him the police would never come to this place?

Simon could not run without being spotted in this large open farmland. His only option was to hide, but he was hemmed in, trapped in the middle of the U shaped yard. He could not walk around the truck without being seen from the driveway, so Simon crept along, almost on his belly, to crawl through a fence into the sheep enclosure.

The tight packed cream-colored bodies of the sheep were larger than they had looked from a distance. Smellier too, Simon whispered reassuringly to them willing them to stay calm. If they got spooked and bolted now, he would lose his cover.

Chapter 4

Alone, Lost in the Alps

For several long anxious moments, Simon crouched between the sheep breathing in the strong sharp smell of damp matted wool, staring at sheep droppings and trying to be invisible.

When the police car drove away and Simon grew brave enough to venture out and back to the truck that he had been working on, his concentration was gone. He worked on Jon's truck for another few hours, but nothing seemed to work. The truck's problems remained no matter what he did.

When Jon arrived Simon explained what had happened, why he smelled like a sheep and that he had been unable to fix the truck. "Never mind," Jon told him. "Let's go home."

Back at the apartment Eugin and Jon both shook their heads this time as Simon related the story in more detail. After speaking with their friend, Durik, they learned that the police had been at the farm to deliver some court documents. There had been no suspicions or questions about illegal immigrants, but the episode had frightened all of them. Simon took to sleeping close by the back entrance to the apartment where he could make a quick escape to the street in case the police came knocking.

When Eugin and Jon went off to church the next weekend, they returned with a friend named Adam. Although a Romanian, like all of them, Adam was also a citizen of Austria for he had obtained his citizenship some time ago. As the four of them visited together into the evening, Simon finally got up the courage to ask Adam if he would be willing to give him a ride to the Italian border.

"Sure. I can take you," Adam agreed. "When do you want to leave? We could leave now if you want."

Simon beamed. A price for the dangerous mission was agreed on, plans to meet were made, and Simon felt hopeful as he stashed some clothing and some food into a new packsack. It was only a four-hour ride to the border and he would be in Italy in the morning. By tomorrow evening he could be eating dinner with his brother, Stefan.

Good—byes were hard to say though. Simon shook hands with Eugin and Jon and thanked them again and again for their kindness. Then he stepped outside into the night to begin what he hoped was the last part of his journey.

In the car Simon used his flashlight to study Adam's maps. Once out of the city they headed northwest up into the mountains. Adam reassured Simon that he would be able to get fairly close to the border, and that they should arrive around midnight, a good time for Simon to find a spot to cross undetected.

They'd been driving almost four hours when Adam pointed.

Simon felt his heart speed up as rows of lights appeared in the distance. The border looked well lit, and wide, and even at this hour they could see the taillights of the cars stopping in a line—up.

Adam stopped to let Simon out while they were still some distance from the crossing. "I must leave you here, my friend," Adam explained. "This is probably the last exit I can take in order to turn back." He leaned over to shake Simon's hand. "Good luck," he said.

Where Adam left him was a risky place to be seen on the highway walking, for Austrians were notorious for calling in anything suspicious. And someone walking along a multi–lane highway like this one would definitely arouse suspicion, especially so close to the border. But Simon had no choice. He tried to walk quickly when he could, looking back constantly, and crouching into the ditch whenever car lights got close to where he was.

He managed to get a good deal closer to all the lights before he discovered that he and Adam had somehow miscalculated. The lights ahead were not part of the border crossing at all. What had appeared to be a border crossing were only tollbooths on the super highway.

Simon had no idea how much farther it was to the border, but he knew he could not travel far enough or fast enough crouching along in the ditch beside the highway. Up ahead he could see that this would not be possible very soon for sheer rock and steep banks sloped down from the highway. Just to continue in this direction he would somehow have to cross the highway and follow along on the other side, but there was no cover over there either and a tall 10 foot fence bordered the road. Simon stared at the fence wondering if he could climb fast enough to get over the top during a break in traffic.

Picture of an autobahn

49

For several moments Simon watched cars speed past, waiting for a break and judging the time he would need to get across. But when he did finally run, his legs were wobbly. They felt clumsy as he urged them for more speed crossing the wide lanes.

In a slight depression between the two highways, Simon threw himself down to lie flat, panting to rest a moment and watch the traffic racing along in the other direction. He would need a much larger break in the traffic this time, because this time he would need to cross three lanes and climb the fence before being spotted. Could he do it?

At the next break in the line of cars heading back towards Vienna, Simon made his move and began running. But as soon as he was up on his feet he could see that there was not enough time to scale the metal fence. He would barely start climbing before the next cars would catch him in their headlights. He'd be trapped between the fence and the traffic, in plain view. A spurt of terror fueled his legs now, and he ran along the fence at top speed, his mind racing. Panic began overtaking his thoughts. *"I'm dead, I'm dead. I'll never make it out of this one,"* his brain insisted as his feet pounded out long steps. The car lights were approaching fast; he would be seen for sure.

"God, help..." Simon yelled into the night. It was all he could manage.

And then he saw it. A hole in the fence! With a frantic burst of speed Simon made it to the opening in the metal mesh and lunged, tearing a rip into his jeans as he scrambled through. As his feet cleared the fence he felt the vibration of the speeding cars rush past and heard the whhhumm, whhumm of the traffic and the heavy smell of exhaust.

Simon let his head fall back against the cold rocky soil. A wonder filled his mind. Like opening a window in a dark room he felt, as if for the first time, that perhaps God *was* with him. God must care about him, Simon, personally. It was such an interesting concept that he had to remain absolutely still just to gather all of it into his mind. Had he doubted it before? He wasn't sure. But it was as if the appearance of that hole had suddenly reinforced his feeble faith; as if he finally comprehended that an all-powerful heavenly King was truly interested in him. Protecting him. It felt like a miracle, his own miracle, much like the stories that missionaries told in church. Warmth filled Simon and he looked up at the distant stars to whisper his thanks.

When the traffic abated once more, Simon hurried farther away from the highway to the cover of some trees.

The border had to be fairly close, he thought, for he and Adam had both studied the map. This highway did go to the border. He felt sure about that. If he kept the highway in sight perhaps he could still get into Italy before dawn.

But the terrain was much more difficult here. The highway occupied the only flat surface through these mountains. Everywhere else was straight up and down. Plus, it was so dark he could barely see where he was placing his feet at times. Sharp rocks and steep places tripped him several times, but he dared not risk turning on his flashlight. For all he knew there were border patrols scouting this area. He couldn't try to sleep or even rest during the darkest hours either; it was much too cold for that option. So he kept walking.

For every kilometer of the highway Simon figured he was putting in at least three or even four kilometers just struggling up and then down and over. Tunnels along the highway blocked out the lights and the noise of the cars as the road sped through a mountainous area two different times. When this occurred, Simon was forced to crawl to the top of each crest, make his way back down into ravines and then climb back up once more.

The only light seemed to come from the highway now. The toll booth was no longer visible behind him, and car lights in the distance seemed to be the only link with civilization. At one point, deep at the bottom of another ravine, the darkness was so complete that Simon felt blind. He could hardly believe that darkness could be this intense. Was the half moon hidden behind mountains here? It was as if a heavy black velvet curtain enveloped him. He could no longer even see his hand as he reached out to feel his way back up the rocky slope. And then, somewhere to his left a wolf began to howl. Simon froze as he heard two more wolves reply, far in the distance.

For several moments, Simon gave in to the terror that he'd been swallowing back. The hole in the fence was forgotten, and it was all he could do to keep from bolting in terror. There could be wolves just a few yards away, silently drooling, tongues lolling out as they watched him. In this pitch darkness he wouldn't see them until it was too late. He'd have little chance of defending himself anyway, especially if they attacked in a pack.

Simon squeezed his eyes tight against the fear and breathed in and out as quietly as he could manage. He tried to recapture the wonder he'd felt just a few hours ago when he realized that God had saved his life. That awe, and that new rush of belief . . .was it such a tiny, brittle faith, that it could snap so quickly? With labored focus he sent his thoughts to God, and forced his limbs to crawl slowly up the sharp boulders in front of him. He couldn't afford to fall. Breaking a leg, or even spraining an ankle could be fatal for him now. He winced in pain as his hand scraped a sharp spot, and then cringed at the crunch of his steps and the noise of some falling gravel. But he kept moving. He wanted to get higher, closer to the highway. He didn't want to be in the bottom of some ravine when the wolves attacked.

The darkness was still absolute when he got to the top. An overwhelming urge to run from the oppressive blackness almost got the better of him. With effort, he constrained himself to go forward carefully.

He was creeping along in the pitch darkness, concentrating on the sound of his own breathing and trying to remember the words of a song when he felt something close. A presence. There was nothing to see, and nothing to hear, but he knew somehow that he was not alone. He could feel the presence of an animal very near.

A bear, he thought. And his heart fell into his stomach. Why hadn't he gotten his knife out? He wouldn't even be able to protect himself. He strained his eyes to see, not able to move. It was so close. It loomed just in front of him, a larger patch of darkness against the dark. It was too big for a wolf. Too silent. It wasn't even sniffing the air. Did bears have poor eyesight in the dark as well, he wondered?

Simon had heard somewhere that you should yell and holler to scare off a bear. But he had too little air or courage to make much of a noise. So he sang instead.

"A song we sing, a song like no other
Its about Jesus. He is alive..."

It was the song he and Wesley had sung as a duet over a decade ago.

"When difficult times, pain and sorrow come
I'll not be afraid
I can trust that He will see me through."

Still singing between his labored breath, Simon slowly maneuvered his flashlight from his pocket and turned it on. He shadowed it with his jacket, just in case anyone was looking this way. But he had to aim the light towards the beast even if he did risk being seen.

And then Simon laughed. It was an odd kind of laugh and it sounded a bit like a sob. He watched as the little group of cattle shifted, and one stood up from where it had been laying. Then they all moved off together without so much as a moo.

Simon switched off his flashlight.

Cows. He'd almost died of fright over cows.

Simon's heart was still beating ferociously though, and he missed the quick reassurance of the light he'd shone out so briefly. The night felt oppressive. He searched the skies for a sign of light, staring, as if he expected the blackness to change its mind at any moment. And then he sighed and looked toward the sound of a vehicle on the highway far to his right.

He wasn't going to make it to the border before light. Not at this rate and right now he didn't care. He longed for daylight more than he longed to reach the border.

The cows had cheered him a bit though. Cattle were let out to range in the spring and they might be quite a distance from their home ranch. But their presence felt heartening. Maybe just over the next ridge he would see the friendly light from a ranch house window. He decided he would risk asking for shelter if he did see some kind of house. He knew whoever lived in a place like this, close to the Austrian border, would phone the police and report him. But weren't the police a better fate than being attacked by wild animals? Wasn't being deported back to Romania better than being torn apart by wolves?

When the sky finally began to lighten Simon was almost too exhausted to notice. His pace had quickened once he could see his path more clearly, but after several hours of strenuous hiking he was so tired his legs were feeling shaky. The cold seeped through him even as he walked, so he couldn't risk stopping. Snow still covered many high areas here and it lay slushy and thick under trees and in parts of his pathway.

He filled his water bottle from a freezing cold stream as the sun crested the mountains and finally reached a touch of warmth down to him. And then, when the sun stood directly overhead, he lost sight of the highway altogether. In the light of day he couldn't' risk walking in sight of the highway in case someone spotted him and he'd somehow ventured too far from the road. Several times he'd had to hike in the wrong direction, away from the highway just to navigate a difficult area. But this last time he'd had to climb around and away from a sheer faced wall of rock near the road to find another passageway up and over a mountain. And now he couldn't see the highway at all. Had he lost track of his direction? Gone too far?

It would be so easy to get lost in these mountains. Simon tried to keep going, using the direction of the sun for guidance and consulting his tiny compass periodically. But the compass didn't seem to be working, and only wilderness met his eyes in every direction. He told himself that he would spot the autobahn as soon as he got over the next rise, or around the next turn, but there was nothing. He was alone and cold, high in the mountains far from any help, and trembling with weariness.

Chapter 5

Stop or We Shoot!

Simon had been listening intently for the sound of the highway when he began to hear what sounded like a waterfall. It grew so loud that he knew the sound of traffic on the autobahn would never carry above such a noise.

He saw it as soon as he crested the next mountain. A river. Still far below him, the angry rush of water ran so fiercely that it filled the entire valley with its roar.

For several more hours Simon traveled down to the river and then along its spirited waters, stumbling over a rocky shore. It was something to follow, but he didn't know if he was even moving in the right direction. There was no way he would ever be able to cross such a deep, fast moving river. Simon might have scanned the noisy rush of water for more likely crossing spots, but he wasn't much of a swimmer, even in calm lake waters.

The sun was already approaching the steep western flank of the Alps when Simon caught a glimpse of a long bridge spanning the river. Relief flooded him as he realized that he'd found the autobahn at last. It was high above the shore, and it took him some time to crawl up level with the highway again. When he'd reached an area of cover close to the bridge, his heart sank again.

It looked impossible to cross the bridge. For several moments, Simon crouched to catch his breath and study the layout of the highway and the bridge. He calculated the length of the bridge, the height of the fences, the traffic load and the timing and then he slumped down a little further and closed his eyes. He didn't have a chance. He would never make it across the bridge without being seen or run over. Even if he waited until full dark, the lights, already shining in the fading daylight, were bright here. To scale the tall fence without being seen would be difficult enough. But the bridge itself was too long, even if he ran like the wind.

Once again Simon studied the river below. He scanned far up the river too, looking for where the grey frothing tumble of water might look calmer or easier to cross. But he'd walked quite a distance along that river already and knew it wasn't likely especially in this season of spring melt. Also, in this steep mountainous terrain, to travel upstream very far would carry the risk of getting separated from the highway again.

For another half hour Simon paced and watched and worried. Then he crawled closer to where the bridge supports plunged down onto the rocky hillside and looked up, underneath the long structure. As the last rays of the sun disappeared behind the mountains, he made up his mind about what he must do.

He would cross the river gorge underneath the bridge. He would grip the piping holds on the underside of the bridge, high above the water, and inch his way to the other side, hand — by — hand. It was his only chance.

After a rather difficult climb down and then up the rocky bank to reach the under parts of the bridge, Simon placed his hands on the rounded pipes, like parts that formed part of the bridge structure underneath. He kicked out and let his full weight hang by his hands, testing it. The pipes were ice cold, coated with fine river stone dust, and almost too wide to grasp comfortably. But they felt solid enough. They would hold his weight and then some; and they extended evenly for the entire length of the bridge at least as far as Simon could see.

Simon found a flat rock and sat to eat some canned salted beef and drank some more water to regain his strength. Then he stood to squint toward the far end of the long bridge, where the struts met the rocky ledge on the other side of the river. From here it looked as though it might be rather tricky to jump down on the other side. Unlike this end of the bridge, which overhung a large area of rocky dry land before it actually was above the water, the other end of the bridge looked as if it met land on a rather steep cliff.

But dusk was already darkening the view, and Simon told himself that it probably looked worse from this far away, especially in this light. And it wasn't like he had a choice for it was too cold to wait out the night here.

He saw his Bible, while fastening his packsack, and stopped his hurry for a moment to lay one hand down on the smooth leather as if somehow the touch might give him the strength he was going to need. Then he secured his pack, rubbed his hands together briskly, put his gloves back on and reached up to hold the cold metal.

Hand-over-hand Simon inched his way from one hold to the next, legs dangling. He wouldn't let himself look down at the frothing river below or think about how far it would be to fall, but he could feel the vastness of space beneath his swinging legs.

When his hands grew too tired and shaky, he pulled himself up higher. Bending his elbows so that he could rest one arm at a time, he held up his body's weight to catch his breath. On one of these rest moments he looked ahead to check his progress and stared in disbelief. His strength was almost gone and he hadn't even made it half way across!

Simon didn't allow himself to look ahead after that. He could not afford to have his courage fail him now. He concentrated on the rhythm of his movements and the hand hold directly in front of him. He didn't allow his mind to dwell on images of plummeting into the ice–cold frenzy of water beneath him. He directed his thoughts instead to picture freedom, and his new life in Italy. He visualized walking down colorful cobble stoned streets with his brother, Stefan. He thought of the two of them stopping at a little restaurant with soft upholstered seats where the strains of beautiful music filled in the spaces around their conversation. Simon imagined tearing open fresh warm bread as he studied the menu, deciding what to order. Later, they might stop to buy ice cream in a grassy park where children laughed and called to each other. He would call home and tell his mother, "I'm here with Stefan. I'm safe now." He pictured going to church with Stefan next, whispering together about the pretty girls sitting across the aisle, and singing praises to God for seeing him through so many dangers.

A gust of wind blew grit into Simon's eyes and the dream dissolved, tearing away like the cobwebs he reached through with his hands. His strength was used up. It felt as if it had been at least an hour since he'd begun this torturous undertaking, and still there was always another handhold, just in front of him. They went on forever perhaps there was no end. Soon he would be unable to hold on, his grasp would slip and he'd fall. But, when those thoughts came he didn't let himself look down or ahead and finally, Simon saw the end of the bridge just beyond the next few handholds.

Getting to the ground was much more dangerous this time. Simon had to let go and jump and then grab out quickly to stop himself from sliding off the rocky cliff and plunging all the way into the river.

When he scrabbled up the rocky face of the cliff and finally rested on solid ground, he felt so drained of strength that he lay with his legs sprawled out and his cheek resting on a cold damp rock. Limp as a child who has been tickled too long, Simon concentrated only on breathing for several moments.

It was full dark when Simon picked up his hiking stride beside the autobahn once more. The terrain had begun to descend and he imagined that it was growing less rugged. He kept the lights of the highway as close as he dared this time, dreading another night of darkness in the wilderness.

The fact that this part of the highway seemed so well lit encouraged Simon to think that perhaps he was close to the Italian border now, and he crept more slowly. Trying to move silently, he winced each time a branch snapped beneath his feet. No matter how slowly and carefully he set down his feet, it was next to impossible to keep the dry underbrush from cracking. Each loud snap startled like a gun shot adding to Simon's fright.

The border surprised him when he finally came to it. There were brighter lights around the building, and he could see the cars slow and stop, but he couldn't see any patrols, or guard towers, or much activity. He hadn't heard much about this border and didn't know what to expect.

The terrain was still forested and steep rocky ridges dotted the area. There didn't appear to be any plowed ground or extensive fencing. But he still waited, leery of what might lie in wait for border runners like him. He watched for at least two hours getting up to move about and pace and blow on his hands to keep warm. He was close enough to see people moving about, cars stopping and car trunks opening. Close enough to feel the sick knot of fear clutch his insides as flashlights swept into the back seats of the cars' interiors and clipped voices barked orders.

Once again he sprinted, alert to every sound and movement as he crossed. It felt easy this time. Had his confidence increased? Had facing so many dangers somehow muted his panic? And where was the second border? In Romania and in Hungary both, there had been two borders.

Simon didn't know if he was still in Austria or finally in Italy even after he began to see the lights of a town ahead. For all he knew he might be still in the neutral zone.

The lights of the town were such a welcome sight after his ordeal in the mountain wilderness that he wanted to run to them. He wanted to walk right into the town and find the train station but he knew he must look terrible. There was a rip in his leather jacket, his jeans flapped open above the back of his knee where he'd torn them getting through the fence and he was dirty and unshaven. His appearance would certainly arouse suspicion. He needed to try and clean himself up a bit. And before he came out of hiding to find a train station he wanted to be sure that he had finally arrived in Italy.

Creeping closer, keeping himself hidden, Simon squinted in the dark, trying to see anything that might help him know where he was. It was too dark to read signs so car license plates might be his best bet, he decided. Ahead he spotted a few buildings near a road and several vehicles parked in front of the buildings. He decided to get closer and take a look at the license plates to see if he was in Austria or in Italy.

There were dogs barking at him as he crept from one shadow to the next, but he kept moving towards where he saw the parked cars. One dog seemed to be tailing him, and his occasional growls were setting Simon's nerves on edge.

Simon could almost make out the numbers on the license plates now. Another few steps and he would know. But it only took one more step to make a shocking discovery. The cars were all police cars. The dogs might even be police dogs!

Behind him, too close for comfort, another dog snarled. With a sudden thud, Simon's heart threw itself against the inside of his ribcage, as if trying to escape. Then in blind terror, his feet responded as he turned and fled. The dog followed, still barking loudly as Simon sped away from the friendly lights of the town, back into darkness. He kept running long after the dog had stopped its alarming noise. His feet pounded on after every sound had faded. The terrain was rocky and steep but it hardly slowed his steps while he ran as if his very life depended on speed. Fear lent him strength.

As he raced up a rocky ridge, loose rock shifted beneath him, his feet slipped and then he was falling. He couldn't stop. Under him a sea of moving rock swept him downwards at an alarming speed. And then suddenly there was nothing below him. He was falling through the cold darkness. His mind felt curiously detached as his arms and legs flailed out helplessly.

He thought, *this time I'm going to die*, but it didn't startle him. He thought of his family, wondering if they would ever know what had happened to him. And he thought of his God. Was he ready to meet his God?

When his hand brushed into something, instinct made him seize hold of it. It was a little tree, rooted into the bank. Simon clung to it with both hands. Small rocks and clods of earth broke away as he bumped against the cliff and waited through a small silence of at least five seconds until they landed, far below. He couldn't see anything of where he was or what lay below him but he knew it was a long fall to the bottom.

With painfully slow movements, Simon inched one leg, and then the other up to test out places that would hold his weight. He'd added another layer of ground in dirt to his jeans by the time he reached the top of the bank, and he'd somehow lost one glove, but he was alive.

Dawn was brushing the clouds with lighter grey to the east now and Simon stood to rest his aching muscles and look around him. He'd lost sight of the lights of the village he'd run from, but from this viewpoint he could see the lights of another town, directly across from him, on the side of the mountain facing him. It would be quite a hike to reach the town from here. He would have to descend one mountain, and climb another to get there but it looked to be a good-sized place, one likely to have a train station.

Another cold river blocked Simon's path at the bottom of the two mountains. Simon groaned and paced along the shoreline a ways, scouting it out for likely looking crossing spots. It didn't look very deep but he knew it would be icy.

With his socks and boots in one hand and his jeans rolled up to his knees, Simon stepped into the river, wincing in pain as his feet slid into sharp rocks and biting his lip as the ice water reached higher to soak through his jeans. The pain dulled by the time he was half -way across, and when he'd reached the far side of the river, Simon could not feel anything of his legs or feet below his knees. They were numb.

Taking a moment to splash water over his face, Simon made an attempt to wash the dirt from his hands before he worked at pulling his socks over toes that had no feeling. He hated to even think about what he must look like, but he felt hopeful again, as if his journey must be almost over. The cold water had chased away his aching fatigue. Climbing back up another mountain was difficult with half frozen feet, but by the time Simon had reached the outskirts of the village he felt warm again.

Italian license plates surrounded him on every street this time and a picture sign pointed to what Simon knew must be the train station. Things were looking up.

He felt embarrassed about his appearance but there wasn't much he could do. The sun was cresting the mountains now, filtering golden sunlight onto picturesque streets and painted houses. People were up and about. A few had already given him strange looks, and he looked down at his dirty ragged clothing wondering if he ought to keep going. But the train station had to be just ahead. He'd duck into a pubic washroom; change some of his clothes and clean up a bit when he got there.

He was walking by shops a few streets later that were just opening. People were passing him on the street, walking to work probably. Most avoided even looking at Simon, but Simon could hardly keep himself from staring at them. They looked different. Two girls passed him in a rush and he turned to take another look as the one with dark curls twirled back to stare at him. A blush showed on her face from half a block away. Her shiny hair, bright yellow scarf and bouncing steps pumped Simon's mood like the first notes of a favorite song.

Two men in a restaurant window seemed to be arguing amiably, eating with their mouths open, and waving their arms, with steaming cups of coffee in front of them. Simon couldn't understand the words but he smiled at the sight of them. Fresh pastries watered his mouth in another window, and he made himself look away from staring an old man sitting on a bench muttering to him self. On the other side of the street a woman and small child had stopped to talk to an older woman wrapped in a bright shawl and the impatient little boy hopped on one foot and then the other. It all looked so normal that Simon had to smile.

He was going to live in this county. He'd made it. It was going to be all right. A grin spread wider on Simon's face as he imagined once more how surprised and happy Stefan would be to see him, but he had to *get* to his brother first. He had to reach the train station.

Sights of fresh produce on an outside display and the aroma of sausages cooking puckered his mouth with hunger, but he was afraid of approaching any merchant. He could not afford to spend any of his Italian lire on food either. He wanted to have enough for the train fare.

The train station, when he finally spotted it, lay on the other side of a wide expanse of tracks and boxcars. Simon picked his way over the tracks as he tried to read the unfamiliar words on the signs around the station. Tarvisio appeared to be the name of the town but there were many words he could not make out. As he approached what looked to be the main building, he stepped up onto the platform and headed for the door. His hand was almost on the door to open it when he veered away at the last moment, and walked right by, as if he'd changed his mind. There were policemen sitting just inside at a table on the other side of a large window. All three policemen raised their eyes to him as he went past, and Simon cursed his carelessness. His only choice now was to keep walking until he was safely out of sight and then run. Perhaps they were too intent on their morning coffee to bother with him. Perhaps they hadn't had enough of a look to notice his disheveled appearance. He couldn't be caught now. Not now when he was finally so near his destination.

He had barely turned the corner when he heard running footsteps. Fear won over good sense and Simon bolted. Behind him he heard a commanding voice yell out, "Stop! Stop or we'll shoot!"

Simon stopped. He raised his hands away from his sides as he turned to face his pursuers. All three had their guns out pointed at him.

Chapter 6

Jail Cell Brutality

Simon's hand began its automatic drift to his left shirt pocket to feel for his ID and then stopped. It wouldn't be good to reach for anything or move much at all with guns aimed at him.

It felt so unreal as though Simon was watching it all happen to some stranger. People had stopped to stare. The policemen were shouting at him, words he didn't understand. He could hardly hear them over the sound of an incoming train, his own heart hammered to escape his chest.

As the three uniformed men approached, Simon began to understand some of their angry shouting. They wanted his ID. "Passport, papers!" Their words struck out at him, like hammers, causing his body to jerk. "Where are your papers? Hand over your ID!" They all seemed to be shouting at once.

Cautiously Simon lowered his hands and reached for the ID he carried in his buttoned left shirt pocket. He was surprised enough to look down at his shirt when he didn't feel the bulge of his ID there. The shirt pocket was still buttoned securely, but his identification was not in the pocket. With frantic hands now, Simon searched all his other pockets.

He struggled for the words he needed to appease the angry men still pointing guns, but he didn't know enough Italian to make them understand. When his faltering responses only made them more enraged, he stopped trying to speak and began searching through his other pockets for the second time. He was honestly baffled at what could have happened to his new driver's license and other ID papers. For weeks now, since he had left home, he had been in the habit of buttoning it securely into his left shirt pocket. The quick gesture of reaching up to check for it there had become a habit in the last few weeks. How could it have fallen out of his pocket if that pocket remained buttoned?

Simon remembered his Italian/Romanian conversation booklet then. Perhaps he could communicate better if he could find the words, or even point at the phrases he was trying to say to them. The heavy-set policemen holstered his gun and grabbed up Simon's packsack just as Simon started to reach for it. He shoved Simon roughly as he took it. Then the taller, older officer waved his gun at Simon and yelled for him to move.

At the police station the yelling seemed to intensify. It was as though they thought Simon were some dangerous terrorist or was purposefully trying to defy them by concealing his ID somewhere. They had confiscated his pack with his language phrase book, and Simon did not have the words or the courage to ask for it. Understanding some of their words, but not having enough knowledge of the language to explain him-self, Simon had to give up trying to speak. Whenever he tried to talk they just screamed the louder so he thought silence might be a better option.

Not answering their demands at all brought a different type of abuse. Simon flinched as hard leather gloves caught him just below his right eye. "Where is your ID?" the taller officer shouted. Another pair of black leather gloves hit him from the other side. His left ear stung and he fought against the impulse to raise his hands and protect his face. They were all slapping out at him now.

Simon didn't know what to do. Attempting to answer that he didn't know where his ID could be in his faltering Italian enraged them, but keeping silent seemed to infuriate them too.

"Where are your papers?" they continued to shout. They were getting rough now. Slapping had failed to bring any results and their blows became more painful.

Then they asked, "Where do you come from?"

Simon understood that question. "Austria," he told them. "I come here from Austria."

More shouting erupted then, and Simon was handcuffed and shoved roughly back through the police station and into a police car.

It took no time at all to reach the border that Simon had crossed what seemed days ago now. The Austrian border patrol escorted Simon into an interrogation room. This time they supplied a translator and Simon answered every question honestly. Fearful that he would be subjected to more beating here, he admitted that he was Romanian when the translator asked. But it didn't seem to matter. The Austrian authorities didn't want to bother with Simon.

When they heard that Simon had been caught in Italy, they decided that he was Italy's problem. "We don't want him. He is your problem," they told the Italian police.

It wasn't what Simon's captors had wanted to hear. In seething anger they traveled back to the Italian police station in Tarvisio. This time the cruelty intensified. In minutes Simon was down on the floor, tasting his own blood in his mouth.

Simon watched as a police officer searched through his leather jacket, inch-by-inch, searching for the ID they felt sure that Simon was concealing from them. He stood shivering, cowering from blows after he was forced to strip down to his underwear while more officers felt through his other clothing.

Angry shouted questions rained down on him again when the officer with the wide girth shook some of Simon's socks in front of his face. They were the new blue socks that Eugin had given Simon in Austria as he was packing. Simon had not worn them yet and the paper tags with Austrian printing still hung from the thick wool. But Simon didn't know what the officer wanted to know. It almost seemed as if the man thought Simon must have stolen the socks. Did having new socks in his possession incriminate him somehow? Simon didn't know.

For several hours Simon was left alone to worry. He was cold in the jail cell, aching in all the places where he'd been punched and slapped and dreading what might happen next. Hunger gnawed at him, too. But the day dragged on, the light faded outside and no one brought him any food. Each time the door opened into his cell, it brought only more screaming and more beating.

With no ID to incriminate him, Simon could not be deported back to Romania. Even if the police suspected that Simon was Romanian, they could not send him there without identifying papers. Simon was too afraid to care at this point. Even knowing that if he was sent back to Romania he would have to serve a lengthy prison sentence for trying to avoid his army duty, he was frightened enough at this point to tell them what they wanted to know. He'd been beaten and threatened so badly that he would have surrendered any ID he had, just to make them stop their painful questioning sessions.

He slept only a little that night, awakening in a cold sweat, queasy with fear. Hope had almost flickered out by the morning. Simon tried to cringe farther into a corner when his captors opened the cell door. He knew the routine by now. First they would scream out their questions, and then they would begin beating him. Twice now, after Simon had been beaten, he laid on the floor, as his tormentors kicked him with their heavy boots. This time when the stocky policeman had finished roughing him up, the atmosphere grew quiet. The younger red-faced officer glared silently at Simon. Anger lit his black eyes with two bright hot sparks, but a smile played at his thin lips. Slowly the young man unsnapped his gun. Pushing roughly, he forced Simon into a kneeling position and pushed his gun against Simon's temples.

Simon closed his eyes and tried to pray but no words would come. He stifled a sob as he heard the gun being cocked. Had God truly forsaken him to this end?

The awaited gunshot blast never came. The two men only laughed, aimed another kick to his ribs and left Simon shivering with shock.

A single bowl of soup was given to him halfway through the second day. When the officers returned to Simon's cell later on, the presence of a police woman seemed promising at first. Simon felt that the officers who had been beating him so cruelly would perhaps respect the presence of a woman and ease up on the rough abuse they had been dishing out. Maybe, being a woman, this police officer would have some compassion when she saw the miserable state of Simon's bruised body. But almost immediately the female officer barked out a question and then smacked Simon painfully with the back of her hand. Simon recoiled in shock, with blood dripping out of his nose.

"Who are you? Where are your ID's?" she shouted.

"I don't know," Simon answered.

It wasn't what any of them wanted to hear. Taking his words and his refusal to cooperate with them as defiance, they continued beating him.

When they came into his cell the next time, he was stripped of all his clothing. There were only two of them this time but when they began beating him Simon longed only to pass out. When a powerful kick plunged into the soft part of his stomach he rolled over and pulled his knees up to gag through the pain as he wondered if something he could not live without might have been ruptured.

He'd been three days in the cell when his clothing was thrown to him and he was told to get dressed. Once again Simon was pushed into a police car and taken to the Austrian border. Once again the Austrian officials refused to accept him.

As his captors roughly escorted him from the building and down the walkway to the police car, Simon felt the eyes of many people watching him. Clean shaven men in late model cars waiting to cross the border. Little children with their heads out the window, tourists with shocked faces; they were all staring.

Simon bowed his head, wanting to disappear as fear was suddenly cast out by shame. He focused on the handcuffs at his wrists as tears sprang into his eyes and embarrassment flushed his face. No doubt everyone staring at him thought Simon was some hardened criminal. What else could they think? A dirty, rough looking guy in hand cuffs being shoved along by several police-men must be a felon. Someone in this situation must surely have done something hideous.

He felt relieved to get pushed back into the police car away from so many curious eyes. But in a few moments, when the car turned away from the highway that led to the police station in Tarvisio, Simon feared the worst. The silence in the car almost deafened him as the red–faced young policeman increased his speed out on the open highway. The heavy-set officer sitting in the front passenger seat handed Simon a granola bar to eat.

In spite of his fierce hunger, Simon found it difficult to chew or swallow with a stony faced officer beside him and a terrible foreboding forming in the pit of his stomach. He began to think now that they were probably taking him out to some desolate area in order to shoot him. Was this crunchy oatmeal bar his last meal? Had the price he had paid for freedom brought him only this bleak finale?

Outside the sun was shining. Little waterfalls jumped from roadside ledges and majestic snow covered mountains framed green valleys. It was all too beautiful to fit with what was happening.

The car sped along a winding highway, through tunnels, alongside the train tracks and up and down through mountainous terrain for almost two hours before it descended down into what appeared to be a much larger city. Udine, the city limits sign read.

Simon began to breathe a bit more easily when the car parked behind several other police cars, and he could see a much larger government building.

Inside Simon was fingerprinted and forced to sign papers. One of the papers, he came to understand, stipulated that within fifteen days he must leave the country.

"Do you understand this?" he was asked.

Simon nodded. Listening carefully and trying to appear compliant, Simon gathered that being caught in Italy after fifteen days would result in prison time in Italy. And that ultimately he would be sent back to Romania.

After all the paper work was completed, Simon followed his police escorts back through the building and outside to where the car was parked. As he approached the police car, however, the older officer stopped him.

"No. Not you," he told Simon.

Dumbly Simon watched the officer get into the front seat of the car this time, as the stocky policeman got into the back. He moved toward the door of the police car as the young driver came up behind him, unsure of what might be happening.

"You," the policeman gestured, jabbing at him. "No."

They didn't want him to get back into the police car?! What was he supposed to do? Was he being let go? Even with the paper Simon had just signed, he wasn't exactly sure what had just taken place.

It could be some sort of trap or maybe a test of some type. Were they waiting to see how he would respond? Perhaps there were sharp shooters waiting on a roof somewhere or different officials ordered to take him into custody here in Udine.

Simon stood, unsure, until the police car beside him pulled away and drove off. Then, with his thoughts still in a jumble, his feet took over and began running. Frightened still that someone might be aiming at him, he zigzagged as he fled. He hardly noticed all the parts of his body that hurt. He didn't think of his hunger. No plan directed his movements. He just ran along alleys, across parks, down deserted sidewalks, and through vacant lots. He ran until there was no more breath in his lungs and he hardly had the strength to remain on his feet.

Apparently no one had followed him. They had really let him go.

Simon tried to feel relieved, but he was still too frightened. He leaned into a cement wall below an iron gateway and struggled for air. Then he looked through his packsack that the police had returned. His Italian money had been taken, but everything else seemed to be still there. He paged through his little Italian language book and found the sentence, "Dove e la statione di treno?" (Where is the train station?)

There was no use worrying about what he must look like, he had to get to a train and leave this place as soon as he could.

In faltering Italian, Simon asked, where is the train station, to the first man who walked past him. But when the man pointed a direction, and Simon smiled his thanks, he didn't feel very confident. Perhaps he had not pronounced the sentence correctly. Or had asked instead for directions to the museum or a place to eat? So Simon asked another pedestrian, just to be sure. When the next person pointed the same as the first, Simon finally believed that he was traveling in the right direction.

He went directly to a phone when he got to the train station in Udine. His brother answered after the first ring.

"Simon, is it really you?" Stefan asked.

"Yes, I am here. I am in Udine," Simon answered. His voice sounded thick and hoarse and took him by surprise, even though it was his own. He told Stefan what had happened with the police "For a few days I did not think it was likely that I would survive," he admitted.

"Don't worry," Stefan told him. "Nobody can touch you for fifteen days. If you have that paper you are safe for now."

74

Simon nodded and murmured a response, but he could not believe Stefan. After the treatment he had just received, trust would not come easily. "They took all my Italian lire," Simon told Stefan. "I have only Austrian and Hungarian money left now."

Stefan explained how and where Simon could exchange his money for Italian lire at one of the exchange machines and then gave Simon the pronunciation of the Italian words Simon would need to buy a train ticket.

"I will give you the address of the pizza restaurant here where I work," Stefan told him. "You may as well come here to find me. I work such long hours I practically live here."

The train Simon needed didn't leave until the evening so Simon had to wait for several hours in the train station. And once the train arrived in the city of Milan, Simon was forced to wait once more. He could not purchase a ticket to Como, where his brother lived, because the train station closed down at midnight and would not open until the next morning.

Outside, the train station did not appear to be a very safe place to wait. Everywhere Simon looked, homeless people stared back at him. Most were rather rough looking characters and some threw menacing glances at Simon as they eyed his packsack. To make matters even worse, police cars made a steady tour of the area every few moments.

Simon didn't know what to do or where to go. He couldn't speak enough Italian to navigate the huge city to a safer spot for the night. He was terrified of being noticed by the police and afraid of becoming lost if he ventured too far from the station. So he settled for a telephone booth within sight of the trains. Rigid with anxiety, he settled himself against one wall to wait out the hours of darkness.

It was barely dawn when the lights came on in the station and Simon could buy a ticket and still very early in the morning when he arrived in the small village of Como where his brother lived.

Simon flagged down a taxi at the station and gave the driver the address of the place where his brother worked. He watched out the car window as the sleepy little village showed its first signs of waking for the day.

Stefan had told Simon how long it would take him to get to Como by train, but he had not taken into consideration the closing of the train station at night. He had expected Simon to arrive at night and he had directed him to go to the pizza place where he often worked until around 2 am.

By Simon's watch it was already 7 am. Stefan would not even come in to work until around eleven so the pizza shop would be closed. Stefan did not have a phone at his home. Simon had only the restaurant's phone number to reach his brother and no way to find out where his brother lived.

He had a new immediate worry as soon as he glanced at the meter running on the dash of the taxi. He had very little money left and it looked as if the taxi fare was adding up quickly. What if the money in his pocket did not cover the fare? Would the driver immediately contact the police? He did not look the type Simon might be able to joke with or ask to wait, and Simon didn't know enough Italian to explain his lack of funds, or dicker over the fare.

I'm so close now, Simon thought. "Dear God, please let me have enough money". With growing unease, Simon drew out his paper money and all of the coins from his pockets as the taxi slowed and came to a stop beside the curb.

At first the driver didn't even turn around. He spoke out the amount of money for the fare so quickly that Simon wasn't sure what the amount was, as he leaned forward to squint at the meter the driver turned around frowning. Slowly he repeated the amount of money that Simon must pay. He stared at the money in Simon's hands and put out his hand to receive the payment.

Simon fumbled, dropped a bill on the floor, retrieved it and began unfolding and handing over the bills one-by-one. When he came to the end of his paper money he began dolling out his coins into the driver's hand with his own hands shaking. He was coming

76

to the end of his funds and he had nothing else he could offer this sour looking man. Once more he glanced at the meter to check the amount and looked down at his last coin in astonishment. He had just enough! It would take his last coin, but he would be able to pay the whole fare.

Breathing deeply after holding back his breath for so long, Simon thanked the driver and stood on the curb watching the white car drive away. Briefly Simon closed his eyes. "Thank–you, Gracious Father", he said aloud. He had no doubt in his mind that a miracle had just occurred. Having the exact amount of money for the taxi was just too incredible to be coincidence. It felt a bit like finding the hole in the fence. God was watching over him, but his faith faltered when he looked around. He couldn't possibly wait outside here for Stefan to arrive for work so he stepped in close to the pizza shop to peer inside. Nothing. There was no one inside waiting for him. No lights were on in the back kitchen either. Everything was dark.

In Milan he had looked like any number of rough looking unwashed vagrants. But in a tidy little village like this, someone in his condition would stick out. From the train station washroom where he'd tried to clean him-self up a little. Simon knew that his face was bruised and his clothes were filthy. The police would spot him and pick him up immediately looking as he did. Someone was sure to report him.

In the growing light of day Simon scanned his new surroundings. Behind the pizza shop, up on a hill, a few houses looked down at the street. They were big houses, mostly two storied. One building looked to be undergoing some renovations.

When he started walking toward the houses on the hill, Simon felt surprised at first. The impulse that made him approach the door of the home where work was being done on the second floor almost alarmed him. He had no reason to believe he could find Stefan here, or that he had any hope of finding his brother by knocking at some random door. His appearance alone would alert any Italian citizen to contact the authorities. At this hour of the day a stranger at the door would be anything but welcome. How could he be so reckless?

But Simon knocked anyway. Something told him it was the right thing to do. Perhaps the miracle in the taxi cab had boosted his confidence because Simon felt sure that God was guiding him.

In spite of the surprising strength of his faith, however, Simon still backed quickly away from the doorway as soon as he knocked. Fear increased the speed of his thundering heart. Whoever opened the door could seal his fate forever. Poised between excitement and anxiety, he waited, ready to flee at the first sign of trouble.

When the door opened and Stefan stood before him, Simon had to reach out to clutch the doorframe to keep his body from collapsing. Joy and relief took even his voice. His mouth dropped as he fell against his brother who guided him inside.

When the rush of first words, questions and exclamations had died down, Simon had a shower and changed his clothes. He let warm water soothe the cuts and bruises as he scrubbed away the dirt. Then he followed Stefan to the public phone down the street to call home and let his parents know that he had arrived in Italy.

It was March 23, 1997 Simon's nineteenth birthday and five weeks to the day since he had left his home in Romania.

Chapter 7

Living in Fear of Being Caught

After what he had survived getting to Italy, Simon believed that he would feel happy just to finally be with his older brother, alive and free. He thought he would never complain again if he could just find work, enough to eat, and a safe place to sleep. But it wasn't true. For one thing he didn't feel very free or safe. Once Simon's fifteen days were up, he was constantly looking over his shoulder, wondering if someone was going to ask for his ID. At any moment he knew that someone might report him or that he might be stopped by the police. He also knew that he would face time in an Italian jail, and then he would be sent back to Romania to prison. It was a terrible future to consider for so many hours of every day.

For another thing, Simon hated working in the pizza parlor where his brother, Stefan, had managed to get him a job. The hours in the kitchen were long, and Simon disliked handling all the smelly raw meats. He found he didn't even like the taste of pizza. It was his first experience with the strange flat food, and it didn't appeal to him at all when he first sampled it.

There was no church in Como that he normally attended either, and Simon missed going to church each weekend. In his present uncertain situation, and after what he had just survived, Simon needed the fellowship of other believers.

"Let's go to Torino," Simon urged his brother. "There are many Romanians there. And it's a bigger place. You might find work with a cabinet maker. We could go to church. Don't you miss going to church? Singing? We might even find some friends from home in the church there."

It didn't take long to convince Stefan. In a few weeks the brothers were packing to leave. They took the train to Milan and then to Torino, and arrived in the city that early evening. At home in Romania, they always attended church even the evening services. So after Stefan and Simon had located the address of the church they hurried to arrive before the end of the evening service. They hoped to find friends, or church members who might help them locate a place to stay, but the church was dark and empty. The sign out front listed only the time for the next morning worship program.

Stefan looked at Simon as if the empty church was his fault. "Now what, little brother?" he asked.

Simon glanced around at the neighborhood homes and up the road to several vacant lots. *"It's warm enough now. Let's just sleep outside, close to the church,"* he suggested. *"It will save us having far to go tomorrow morning to come back here to church."*

The weather had improved in the last week and it was warm enough at first. Simon and Stefan found a private grassy spot behind a garage on the edge of a sloping ravine bordered by vacant land. The ground was soft, the stars glittered with promise, and they talked together about what their new lives in Torino would be like.

Stefan had come to Italy illegally as Simon had, but several years before, the Italian government had granted amnesty to illegal persons. Stefan had resident status in Italy now. Instead of settling for a job making pizza, Stefan was hoping to obtain work in his profession as a cabinet maker. It would be easier for him to find such work now, with his proper documents. Simon, without legal identity papers, would have more difficulty. But he, too, felt hopeful as he fell asleep looking up at the stars.

They both woke well before dawn, chilled to the bone. But it was church time, and they were looking forward to go to church so they dressed in their good clothes and cleaned themselves up as best as they were able. Not wanting to lug their belongings into the church, they pocketed their money and decided to leave the rest of their things hidden in the bushes close to where they had slept. Eager to worship with fellow believers, they arrived at the church much too early and had to stand around waiting for almost an hour before a deacon arrived to open the doors.

The wait was worth it, however. It had been too long since either brother had been able to worship at a church they normally attended. It felt like home. The singing of familiar hymns brought tears to Simon's eyes. As much as he wanted to join in with the music of praise, the feelings that welled up inside of him filled his heart so full that he could barely choke out any sound. The language spoke from the front was Italian, and Simon was still unable to understand very much, but the songs were familiar tunes, and there were many Romanian church members in attendance to make them feel at home. One or two of the morning groups offered the choice of study in the Romanian language, and Simon welcomed hearing God's word spoken in his native tongue.

Several of those who attended the Torino church were familiar to Stefan and Simon. The brothers recognized them from home, years ago. Everyone was friendly. A few gathered around them after church, asking questions. When one Romanian man heard that they had just arrived and had not found anywhere to stay yet, he offered his own small apartment.

"I am going back to Romania," he told Stefan. "You are welcome to stay at my place while I am away. I am sure my roommate would not mind."

Simon and Stefan were very grateful. Simon was especially happy to learn that their benefactor's roommate worked in construction and might be able to find a job for Simon there where he worked.

Things were looking good until the brothers returned to their sleeping spot and discovered that their bags had all been stolen. Everything was gone. Regret filled them as they searched, kicking through the long grass and examining the area down into the ravine for things the thieves might have thrown away or left. But it was no use. All they had left was the clothing they were wearing and a bit of money in their pockets.

"My camera!" Stefan shouted. "I knew I should have taken it with me."

Simon stood, uncertain, as he watched his older brother pace. For him the loss did not matter so much. He had lost the things that were dear to his heart already when he had abandoned the packsack his mother had made for him and most of its contents behind the wheels of a truck back in Vienna. He did understand what Stefan must be feeling and came closer when his brother crouched down in the grass, staring at nothing and shaking his head.

"All the letters," Stefan whispered. "From Mam, and... everyone... And my pictures!" He pushed out an anguished breath and looked up at Simon. "Whoever took them would have no use for most of what was in there."

Simon nodded his understanding. He knew that Stefan had been writing to a girl in Romania for some time. He knew those letters had been especially precious. A camera and a cassette player, music tapes and clothing could be replaced. Although it was a great loss and would take more money than they could earn for many months, they could buy more eventually. The personal pictures, the letters, the small treasures and the mementos from home, were all irreplaceable.

The experience discouraged Stefan. He wasn't sure any longer if they had made the right decision in moving away from Como and a secure job.

Fortunately Simon managed to get work in construction that very week.

They were able to keep staying in the apartment too. When the man who was renting the apartment came back from Romania, he told them they could take over the rent payment and stay there indefinitely if they wished. He had brought his family back to Italy with him from Romania and had found a larger place.

Eventually Stefan found work in a cabinet shop, too, and life settled into long days of work and a welcome day of rest each weekend. The brothers began to sing together performing special music regularly at that church, and many other churches in town.

**Simon working
in construction**

**Stefan & Simon
singing in Italy**

Simon began to feel more at ease in this foreign country. He started to pick up more and more of the language, and adopted the styles and mannerisms of the Italians around him. To blend into the culture, he even began using his hands when he spoke.

He never lost his fear of being arrested, however, week after week Simon woke before dawn to begin his long day of work. Often he had to catch a bus before five in the morning, and sometimes he had to transfer buses several times to get to a

83

construction site. But what wore him down even more than the long hard days of physical labor was the constant anxiety. The terror of getting caught haunted him; he could never relax. Always he was wary, watching the people around him. He tried always to speak Italian and not Romanian on the buses or anywhere in public, and he worked hard to blend in. He grew his hair and began wearing it in a ponytail as many of the men did in Italy. He dressed and acted as the Italians did, so that he wouldn't be noticed or singled out as a foreigner. When he asked a question or exclaimed over anything, he used hands gestures automatically just from watching other Italians converse. Simon knew however that none of his efforts would make any difference if someone stopped him or asked for his ID. Looking and talking like an Italian might prevent someone from suspecting him, but it would not bring him any closer to having the right papers to display if he were asked to produce identification.

Late one afternoon, weary from a long day of work, Simon felt fortunate to slump down into an empty seat on the bus. He was thankful for being able to sit down for a change on the usually crowded transport, and he immediately began daydreaming about what he would fix to eat when he got home. Every muscle in his body was crying for rest, but Simon had scarcely felt his body unwind when he heard the question of his nightmares.

"Where is your ID?" the voice asked. It was a high-pitched male voice speaking in Italian, and now Simon knew what those words meant.

"Can I see your passport," the voice persisted. He seemed to be close, maybe only a few seats behind Simon. No doubt he was the agent checking for bus tickets for they often asked for ID if they had any suspicions.

Tired muscles instantly tightened and Simon felt his teeth clench down hard on his tongue as he turned slowly to find the questioner in the sea of faces behind him. He could not see the man yet, but he could hear his voice. Silently Simon rebuked himself for not taking the time to look around. He'd felt proud of the way he could usually spot those who rode the buses, checking that passengers had purchased a ticket and asking for ID. With their no nonsense expressions and their confident manner, they'd become easy for Simon to identify even before they flashed their badges. He'd become well practiced at quickly leaving the bus any time he saw one of them as if he'd changed his mind about where he was going. He always left the bus when he noticed such an official waiting to board.

This time though, the man had been already on the bus when Simon got on.

The unfortunate person who was being interrogated now may not have even looked evasive. Perhaps the man asking the questions was just following some kind of orders in a new attempt to discover felons as he checked for bus tickets. Perhaps he had simply detected a foreign accent and decided to ask for legal papers. Or it could be that he, like many others in Italy, had a personal vendetta against all foreigners.

Simon knew there were many in Italy illegally who were from other countries. Many were criminals causing all sorts of security problems. The amnesty Stefan had received some time ago, and that Simon longed for, seemed to be growing more and more unlikely in light of the crime problems that had been escalating with the number of illegal residents now in Italy.

Simon's grip tightened on his jacket as one hand reached over to push the button on the pole in the aisle to let the driver know he wanted to get off at the next stop. The familiar 'bling' sounded, and the light came on to alert the driver to stop, but Simon could not see a stop ahead. He scanned the roadway, hoping desperately that the next stop would come before the interrogator reached him. "Stop the bus, stop the bus", Simon mouthed anxiously. "Dear Lord, please don't let me be taken here. Not now."

The last time that he had heard someone being questioned on the bus, it had been the weekend and Stefan had been traveling with him.

The man checking for tickets and papers had come directly to Simon, but Stefan had stepped in front of his younger brother at the last minute. He'd assumed an almost aggressive stance, and the man had been forced to deal with Stefan first, and demand his identification. The ruse had distracted the man long enough for Simon to slip off the bus without being questioned and Stefan, with his papers all in order, had been safe.

But Stefan was not here to help now.

Simon closed his eyes. He didn't know if he could survive the consequences if he were to be apprehended now. Could he endure an Italian prison? Was he strong enough for interrogation and constant beatings? His mind rebelled at the thought of being sent back to Romania for more punishment after all this time.

Beads of sweat stood out on his face, and dread filled him as he heard the questioner moving on to ask another passenger for his papers.

"This could be bad. This could be very bad", Simon heard the voice in his head say. And then he was on his feet. It was as if his body reacted without his consent. To avoid looking too suspicious, Simon forced himself to move politely through those standing in the aisles. He strolled indifferently to the front of the bus and stopped there, as if he were only preparing to disembark at the next stop.

It didn't look good though. He had meant to wait until the bus stopped before he stood up to leave, and he felt exposed standing by the door. The bus was picking up speed, weaving through traffic, not even close to a stop. What if he had only made things worse? What if the person grilling the young man a few aisles back grew more interested in Simon now, thinking he looked guilty or was trying to escape?

Bravely he turned to look towards the people facing the front of the bus trying to look innocent. Perhaps if he looked only curious to see who was being questioned it would appear as if he were someone with every right to be here in Italy riding a public bus. If he faced the questioner instead of cowering it might appear as if he had nothing to fear for himself.

Simon saw at once the well-dressed bald man with the red face asking the questions and the flustered dark skinned man searching through his bag in the seat ahead. Even from the front of the bus he could see the terror in the young man's eyes as he fumbled to produce the papers that were being demanded. Simon even had time to feel some compassion for the man as he apparently did not have the required papers.

Pity for the young man who had been caught was not as strong as the relief that flooded him, however. This red faced man whose job it was to check to see if tickets had been purchased or stamped correctly for the correct fare also had the authority to take someone to the police or detain a suspect until the police were called. He would not be able to look around for his next victim to interrogate if he was busy making an arrest.

Simon could hardly keep his legs from speeding away when he finally got off the bus. What slowed him down though, and what prevented him from running, was not his good sense, but his trembling body.

When a shop doorway presented itself a block down the street, Simon slunk into the cement recess in the building and slid down the smooth cool wall to sit on the dirty ground. Farther up the street Simon could hear gunfire. People shooting at each other again, he thought with a shiver of despair.

This was not the better life Simon had pictured. It wasn't the freedom he had longed for. This was a nightmare that he had to live, day after day.

Tears of frustration blurred his vision while Simon sat waiting to overcome his fear, hugging his knees against his tired body. What was he going to do? What could he do?

Finally, when hunger began to gnaw him, he stood up and began walking to another bus stop.

The scenario wasn't an isolated event, however. It happened over and over again. Every other week Simon would either hear the dreaded question, would see one of the ticket checkers board the bus and have to quickly get off, or would simply see someone he thought might be looking at him suspiciously. Always he vacated the area or disembarked the bus as hastily as possible to avoid a confrontation.

Just walking down the street or waiting for a bus caused Simon to constantly look around for police, or "*carabinieri*". If he spotted police, or anyone who looked as if they might be checking him out, Simon would change directions as soon as he felt it was safe and go into a shop, hide in a doorway, or even travel for some distance in the wrong direction to avoid being noticed.

There was a danger of being reported at any time as well. Those who were unable to find work or a place to stay felt jealous of illegal persons like Simon who had found both a job and an apartment. Just to eliminate a bit of competition for jobs, or out of spite, they could turn you in to the authorities. It wasn't safe to let anyone find out you were in the country illegally.

Simon lived in fear most of his days, never knowing when he left for work in the morning if he would be returning home that evening or if he would be looking at the dreary wall inside a jail cell instead. Traveling by bus to church was a risk, too. Simon would often grab his jacket and take a goodbye look at his older brother, when simply stepping outside his apartment to walk to the nearby store. Each time he left the apartment he knew he might never make it back there again.

Chapter 8

Military Orders

While Simon left for work each morning in Italy, unsure if he would return home that day, fearful every hour of being caught, Vasile (Wesley) battled his own problems back in Romania.

Like many other Christian young men, Wesley had contemplated leaving Romania often as he approached the age for army service. He was home with his sister Iulia when his first letter from the army arrived in a parcel of mail a neighbor brought to the house. Wesley watched concern change the shape of his older sister's eyebrows when she held the military envelope. To keep her from worrying, Wesley endeavored to make light of the orders. He joked to Iulia that he had lots of time yet before he would have to jump to army commands or worry about military service.

But Wesley did worry. He didn't speak of it often, but many times his mind went running off in several directions, thinking and searching for some way of escape. Lying awake the night after he received his notice, he weighed the risks of going over the border on foot, across the mountains.

It could be done, Wesley told himself. Simon had succeeded. Wesley had heard of his escape from Simon's father at a wedding where Wesley's singing group had performed. Simon had fled Romania over a year ago probably even before he had received his orders from the army.

Wesley let his mind picture Simon, the way he had looked before they both went onstage to sing, years ago. Back then, Simon had been frightened of singing in front of such a large crowd, but he hadn't been too afraid to take on the dangers of crossing the borders and the mountains on foot. As far as he new, Simon was living in Como, Italy with his brother, safe from worries of army life.

Wesley punched his pillow once more and rolled over to face his bedroom widow. A shiver traveled through his body as he watched the autumn wind moving the trees in the darkness of the back yard. He didn't know if he had the courage to flee across the border alone. He had no idea of the route to take or how to survive the miles of forests and the rugged Alps.

As much as possible, Wesley put the army out of his mind after that. His days were busy with work, friends and music. He worked with his father making cabinets and doors from their home. He helped his mother daily with chores around the house bringing water, cutting wood, and feeding livestock.

Wesley with his parents

Wesley with his friends

And he sang. Always he sang. As well as singing for various churches and at many youth gatherings, Wesley played and sang often with his band, traveling to places to sing for church events and earning some extra money singing and playing at weddings. His life was full.

When the second notice for army service came, however, Wesley could no longer distract himself from thinking about military orders. He knew he couldn't put the orders aside much longer and very soon he would have to decide on either serving in the army, going to jail or escaping. The call to duty in the army was not going to go away, and he would have to act soon. Now whenever he could, he asked around in safe places about how he might obtain a travel visa. They were almost impossible to acquire for someone like Wesley. It would have to be obtained on the black market, and a person needed the right connections. Travel visas' were also extremely expensive. A man earning a decent salary could work for an entire year to earn the almost 2000 German marks Wesley would need to buy such a thing.

Someone Wesley already knew, a friend from his church named Gurd, had managed to get a travel visa for his cousin and another friend to leave the country once. It was rumored that he had connections with an Austrian ambassador. When Wesley asked about obtaining a visa, Gurd just put him off for the price of freedom demanded more than just money. It was a risky business.

He was late for supper on the day that the third military letter arrived. He'd been practicing with his band, getting a few new songs ready for a wedding on the weekend, and he arrived home after dark, to find his sister waiting for him at the door.

Iulia's face looked solemn

"What is the matter?" Wesley asked. "Is it Mama? Is her asthma worse?"

Iulia shook her head no.

"I couldn't get away sooner," Wesley explained. He closed the door on the sharp October wind and took off his jacket. "You know how Alik is. He's always thinking we need to play it one more time." Wesley rolled his eyes as he studied his sister's expression. "Why the long face? Did you eat all my supper or something?"

"No," Iulia answered. Then she took in a breath. "Claudia stopped by with our mail today," she said.

Wesley felt the warmth drain from his cheeks. The good feelings his music had created disappeared like summer rain on an unpainted porch. A cold stone flopped over in his stomach as Iulia held up the letter with the familiar green stripes and the army stamp.

"It's the third one," Iulia told him.

"I know." Wesley sighed and leaned one shoulder against the big old pump organ just inside the doorway. He waited; giving Iulia space to say more to scold him or tell him what he ought to do, but the space between their words only grew deeper. Wesley reached out to take the letter from his sister. He felt his eyebrows move towards each other as he studied the words. "I better report in," he said softly. "I'll have to go for the medical I guess." Then he stared past Iulia to the doorway of the kitchen where his mother stood watching him. Even from here, Wesley could tell that she had been crying.

He went by train and then by bus into the city to the medical center used by the army. He knew the route well. He'd spent many hours traveling in just the same fashion to his music theory, and singing lessons some time ago. But those trips had been about music, something he enjoyed. This trip brought only anxiety.

Fifteen other young men stood waiting for the doctor when Wesley arrived on the specified day and hour for his medical examination. Two or three of the young men joked around with each other and spoke together in whispers as though they were simply waiting to enter a café to eat. But most of the others shifted their feet, stared at their papers, and avoided looking at each other. Wesley concentrated by looking at his feet and kept his

92

nervousness from showing by practicing the words of a new song over and over in his head.

It was late by the time Wesley boarded the train to go home. He was tired, but he knew he would not fall asleep. It suddenly felt so desperate. Time was short. His name was on the list to report for duty. It might be only a matter of a few weeks before he would have his official orders telling him when and where to appear to begin his army service.

Staring into the dark outside, Wesley prayed silently for God's direction. "How can I serve you if I am in the army, Lord? How can I worship you and do your will? Show me what to do."

For several days Wesley performed his daily activities in a haze of worry and then he received an answer to his prayer. His friend Gurd came to visit and he told Wesley that he was going to be married.

"Aleen and I would like you to sing at the wedding," Gurd told him.

A slow grin crept into Wesley's face. "I would be happy to sing at your wedding, old friend," he said. "And I think you already know what price I will ask."

Gurd nodded. His voice lowered, even though the two were alone. "The price for a visa is higher than ever now," he said. "At least 2000 German marks."

"I have been saving," Wesley told him. "I can get the money."

"Okay," Gurd agreed. "No promises. But I'll see what I can do."

With Wesley of an age for military duty it was impossible to obtain a travel visa from Romania. So Gurd, through his contact, began arranging to get a travel visa from Hungary, from the Austrian embassy there.

To pay for the expensive visa, Wesley sold his scooter to bring in some more money. He took on extra work and gratefully accepted donations from friends and family. Then, when Gurd

93

contacted him, he handed the small fortune over without any hesitation.

He began planning what to take and how to travel even before the visa was in his hands. He hoped that he might be able to hear of someone who would be traveling to Hungary or even Austria, but he had almost resigned himself to taking the bus when his sister Iulia came home from her librarian job with good news.

"I found you a ride," she told Wesley. Her brown eyes shone.

"A ride? With whom?" Wesley asked.

"His name is Arnaldo and he is the nephew of my boss," Iulia said. "He has already agreed to take you."

Wesley stood up. Could it be true? "Is he traveling across the border?" he asked. "When is he going?"

Iulia stole a glance to where their mother sat sewing. Her voice had lost its earlier note of excitement. "Saturday night," she answered. "He's leaving here Saturday night."

Wesley watched their mother turn her face and then rise to leave the room. His heart hurt seeing the way she moved. She had dropped the material she had been sewing onto the floor when she stood from her chair. She probably didn't want them to see her tears. Wesley's own voice cracked a bit when he turned back to Iulia. "This Arnaldo... He is not afraid to take me?"

Iulia was still watching their mother. She shrugged. Her dark blonde hair swung loosely over her shoulders as she turned back to look at him. "I don't know," she said softly. "I told him that you have a travel visa."

"How much does he want?" Wesley asked. "Did he tell you how much he will charge me to take me over the border?"

"He asked for 200 German marks."

"So much?"

Iulia grabbed at Wesley's sleeve. "But he will take you all the way to Italy," she told him. "He lives in Italy."

"Italy?" Wesley could hardly believe it. He grinned back at his older sister. Her brown eyes were sparkling, happy to have

94

helped. But as he stared into them his throat tightened to see them fill with tears and begin to spill over.

"It's only three days away, Wesley," Iulia whispered. "How can we let you go?"

Wesley squeezed her hand and turned away. The sudden ache in his heart traveled up to beat in his throat and he knew he shouldn't risk speaking. He was grateful for such a good opportunity. He hadn't even hoped for a ride all the way to Italy.

After so many months of anguish, worrying how to avoid the army service, his relief at having a plan of escape was intense. It was like being able to breathe deeply out in the clean air again after only taking shallow breaths in a stuffy room. But in spite of his relief something ached with emptiness he had never before experienced. He would be leaving his family, maybe forever. He might never be able to return.

When he awoke the next morning, and remembered what he was about to do, Wesley experienced a stab of something between fear and excitement.

All through breakfast, the thought of leaving created a heavy, crushing weight on his chest. He sat for a long while at the table, looking around the kitchen, dribbling more honey on his bread and talking to his mother as she chopped vegetables. A jar of plum jam sat on the table, unopened, and Wesley twirled the little jar around in his hands. He knew his mother had put the jam out for him. Staring at the deep wine color of the fruit, Wesley felt a lump form in his throat remembering the happy evenings he'd spent with his mother staying outdoors late into the night stirring the huge pot of plum jam over the open fire.

When his father went into the shop adjoining the house, the lights dimmed as they always did when his machinery started up, and Wesley almost choked on his bread at the comforting familiarity of it. His home had never felt so dear. He had never loved his family more.

It was as if he could suddenly see things in a new way, and he gazed around at objects like someone who had been given only a few days to live. Had his mother always worn her hair twisted up on her head like that? Had her eyes always crinkled crookedly at the corners when she smiled? Had the sun slanting over the table turned the edges of the crème bowl into shining gold on other mornings too?

His senses were brand new, hearing as if for the first time the musical sound of the little creek as he crunched over the frosty bridge in the front yard. The haunting way the church bells echoed brought a prickling into his eyes, and the smells of the woodpile as he chopped wood for the fire flooded him with memories. He etched all of it into his mind lingering over the taste of every detail and storing it away somewhere inside himself so that he would never forget.

Chapter 9

Alone in a Foreign Land

Snow fell all day Saturday, November 17, 1998, on the day Wesley was to leave. The whole town felt muffled in silence. Wesley returned home from church with his family in the late afternoon, and stopped to shake the snow from his boots outside the house.

Dinner, typically a happy, noisy event for the whole family, was much quieter than usual. The mamaliga, one of his favorite foods, stuck in Wesley's throat so that he could barely swallow the rich cornmeal dish. His stomach protested over a second helping of the cabbage rolls his mother had made especially for his last meal at home.

Just before he was to meet his ride, Wesley's family gathered together for worship the way they had always done at the end of the day, but even Wesley's father had a tremor in his voice as he prayed. They prayed by turn, pleading for Wesley's safety. On either side of him Wesley's mother and sister held his hands, squeezing tight. There were more than a few tears shed, and it was hard to let go when Wesley's mother hugged him.

It was unlikely that Wesley would be able to come back to Romania. It could be the last time he would have worship with his family and all of them were thinking the same thing. Wesley could see the concern in their eyes as he looked around the circle at them. But no one spoke of such dark possibilities; instead they talked of God's love, His protection and His promises. Iulia read from Isaiah.

Wesley watched the snow falling by the outside light as his sister's clear voice filled the warm room. *"Fear not, for I have redeemed you; I have called you by name, you are mine. When you pass through the waters I will be with you; and through the rivers they shall not overwhelm you; when you walk through fire you shall not be burned, and the flame shall not consume you."*
Isaiah 43:1 & 2

He could not even picture what his life might be. Everything about his life would be different in the space of one week. But whatever happened, he knew that God would be with him.

A few hours after sundown, Wesley said his good–byes bravely and carried his suite case through the deep snow along the roadway by his home and out to the main road to meet Arnaldo. The snow was too deep on the side roads for Arnaldo's compact automobile known as a "Citroen".

Wesley had gone to meet Arnaldo at the library two days earlier, but in the evening light the tall Italian looked almost foreboding as he got out of the car and stood watching Wesley walk towards him. His long dark hair fell over his face as he motioned for Wesley to put his suitcase in the back. In the dim light of the street lamp his dark eyes appraised Wesley critically.

"Did you dress up like I told you?" he asked. "You wear a suit?"

Wesley nodded and opened his coat to show Arnaldo the suite and tie he had on.

"Good. Good," Arnaldo said. He said something about the car's heater, told Wesley again about his buddy that they would be picking up in another city, and then didn't seem to feel like talking.

Wearing a suit and a tie might be a good idea, Wesley decided. If the guards who checked over their papers at the border bought the story that Arnaldo had suggested, the story that Wesley was going to Italy to attend a concert being so dressed up would make the tale more believable. But would it be enough? Arnaldo seemed quite sure that it would work, but Wesley could tell that he was worried too.

They had only been driving the snowy roads for about half an hour when they stopped again so that Wesley could say good–bye to his older sister, Ileana. Although Ileana had not lived at home since Wesley had been very young, there were more tears shed as his married sister hugged him tightly and wished him God's blessing. There was no time for many words.

When Arnaldo's friend, Kahn, joined them in Satu Mare, Wesley moved into the backseat. He tucked his hands under his legs for some warmth and sat up straight staring out at the moonlight on the snow and the dark shadows of buildings and trees.

The words of a song he'd been writing tumbled about in his head, and he hummed quietly to himself to release them loosening some of his anxiety in the process.

At the Romanian border Wesley leaned forward into the light of the guard's flashlight and handed over his travel visa for inspection. He smiled nervously as the guard read the visa and then peered long into Wesley's face. He'd been ready with a well-rehearsed explanation of his "story", but after only a moment, the guard waved them on.

Wesley let loose a deep pent up breath as the car moved past the border.

"One down!" Arnaldo shouted back at him. But he and Kahn seemed as genuinely relieved as Wesley that the Romanian border was now behind them.

They drove through the night.

Arnaldo had been on this route many times and he sped through Hungary talking loudly with his friend, Kahn, while he waved his hands, looking at the road and little else around him.

Wesley looked around at everything. He couldn't sleep.

At the Austrian border, the guards seemed to want more explanation. Arnaldo talked a lot. Too much Wesley thought. He laughed once or twice and pointed at Wesley, too, but Wesley couldn't understand anything they said. He watched the back of the lanky man's head and shoulders for signs of tension and tried to appear unconcerned whenever the guards turned their gaze on him. He'd heard that the Austrians were very strict. Few tried to immigrate to Austria from Romania because of the tighter rules and control. Rumor had it that even ordinary citizens were diligent at reporting illegal immigrants in Austria.

Wesley stared at his hands, surprised to see them trembling. His stomach tightened as the seconds dragged on, but in spite of the guard's wary looks, they too, let them go on their way without so much as examining their luggage.

Austria looked different from Hungary and Romania. More prosperous. The roads were better. They looked well cared for, and everything appeared clean and tidy. Wesley turned back to look at new cars he'd never seen, and stared out over beautiful parks and rows of fine homes with manicured yards. He fell asleep thinking of how his new life would be better, too.

When the car stopped he stirred awake. "Where are we?" he asked.

Arnaldo waved a hand in dismissal. "Nowhere. We're not anywhere. Go back to sleep. I'm going to sleep, too."

They were eating the food they had brought along when Arnaldo woke to begin driving once more. The sun was shining high above them melting the snow into slush. Wesley gawked as Vienna came into view and he craned his neck looking out at the towering mountains ahead.

When they ascended high up onto the mountain roads, Wesley shook his head in wonder at the deep snow piled on the sides of the road and at the rugged terrain beside the high winding highway. He felt very glad he had not decided to make this journey on foot. He tried to calculate how long such a trek would have taken him and shuddered, imagining. Surely Simon had not taken this route in the winter, he thought.

Arnaldo kept up to the speed of the traffic on the autobahn. He changed lanes frequently, and he scared his passengers more than once swearing loudly at other drivers. They were getting to Italy in record time.

Although Wesley grew accustomed to Arnaldo's driving, he started to worry about what would happen next for him. What would he do when he arrived in Italy? As they came closer to the border his mind ran through all of his options, but he couldn't find many. For so long, escape from Romania had been all he had worried about. The problem of getting out of Romania, and his army duty had filled his mind. He'd had little energy left to worry over the next steps and now he began to think that there was a great deal more he hadn't thought through.

Other than a few words and phrases that he had memorized, Wesley didn't speak any Italian. He probably wouldn't even be able to make himself understood in order to find a place to stay or food to buy or someone to give him work. If they all spoke as rapidly as Arnaldo, he would have a difficult time learning the language, too. Would he even know how to buy a train ticket or be able to read signs well enough to find his way around? Where would he sleep tonight?

Wesley hoped the anxiety he'd worked up didn't show in his face as he handed his travel visa to the guard at the Italian border. It wouldn't look good to act afraid or nervous here.

In the front seat Arnaldo was speaking in Italian. The guard listening didn't look amused when Arnaldo laughed and gestured to Wesley. He spoke briefly to Kahn and leaned in to gawk at Wesley once more.

Then the guard simply walked away from them, still holding their ID. Arnaldo swore under his breath and Wesley's heart seemed to quit beating as the guard moved close to another guard to show their papers and gesture to their little Citroen.

To calm his panic, Wesley took up his humming once more letting the words of a song form a prayer in his heart. In the front seat Kahn's fingers drummed noisily on the window ledge of the car.

Arnaldo turned his head sideways to speak to Wesley. "They can't detain you. You have a travel visa. It's a legal document. Don't worry," he said. But the lines of Arnaldo's face had grown hard and still as if he had put on a mask. He lowered his voice and said, "They have no choice. They can't turn you back when you have a travel visa." He seemed to be convincing himself as he hissed out the words.

Wesley's hands began to feel moist with sweat. He reminded himself of the words of the text that his sister had read for worship the night before, ". . . *when you walk through the fire you shall not be burned. . .* " Was he about to face the fire part, already?

When the border guard returned and handed back their ID the silence was so potent that Wesley didn't think any of them were breathing. And then when the gloved hand motioned for them to continue and the car moved past the guard houses, noise burst from all of them. Wesley's concerns about where to sleep that night were forgotten as a raucous levity bounced through the speeding car. Kahn thought up jokes that he told loudly, intermingling Romanian and Italian words and laughing riotously at his barely remembered punch lines.

Not understanding, but strangely relaxed, Wesley laughed with them. The sound fluttered up his throat like the release of a startled bird.

Arnaldo boasted about his girlfriend, and began singing out some repetitive drinking dirge kind of song. Wesley leaned forward when Arnaldo and Kahn tried to outdo each other, remembering mischief they'd done during their days of high school.

The sun had crept behind the tall mountains by the time the car stopped at the train station in Mestre.

Wesley got out of the car and placed his suit case on the uneven pavement. With an awkward smile on his face, he leaned back to the car to say his good–byes.

But Arnaldo just waved away his words of thanks. He said a few words to Kahn in Italian and then got out of the car. He shrugged and offered Wesley a grin. "I'll help you buy that train ticket to Milan," he said. And then he started moving towards the train station, striding ahead as Wesley grabbed his suitcase.

Wesley felt extremely grateful for the help. The station would have been confusing enough even if the words on the signs had been in Romanian. He shook hands with Arnaldo and thanked him once more for his help. Then, clutching his ticket he made his way onto the train.

Darkness had covered the countryside, and there wasn't much to see out the train windows as the locomotive sped towards the city of Milan. But at the huge metropolis that was the Milan train station, there was too much to see. Wesley stared about in wonder and bewilderment at the changing signs, the number of trains, the crowds of people and constant movement. He felt his mind crunch down in concentration as he tried to remember what Arnaldo had told him to ask. But it was gone. He didn't remember the right words to inquire how to go to Torino.

He'd heard that Torino was the place to go in Italy. Many Romanians had apparently made their homes in Torino, but how could he know which train was going to Torino from here? The place was so vast, and everything was moving so fast.

In stammering Italian, Wesley attempted to ask for help, but his grasp of the language was fragile, and no one seemed to understand him.

"Do you speak English?" one gentleman asked.

Wesley shook his head. *"No. Only Romanian."*

The man moved on and another paused to listen to Wesley's faltering words a moment later. "Do you speak French?" the man asked.

Once again Wesley shook his head "No, I speak only Romanian," he said.

Finally someone seemed to understand that Wesley wanted to go to Torino and pointed to a certain location. By the time Wesley had managed to get to the spot, the train had just closed its doors to leave.

It was very late when he finally arrived in Torino. The station was not as huge as the one in Milan, but the place was still daunting. Crowds flowed from one area to another, jabbering ceaselessly words that Wesley could not understand. A rush of alarm traveled through him. He'd had trouble just getting directions to take the right train. How would he ever be able to ask for help to find a place to stay? Where should he go? What could he do?

Holding his suitcase in front of his body to wade through the crowds, Wesley felt weariness wash over his body. He was so tired; he longed for his own bed, the familiar sound of his own language.

And then he heard voices speaking Romanian.

Bravely he followed the sound and stood uncertainly near the men who were speaking. It was clear immediately that the three Romanians were drunk, but Wesley was so relieved to find people whom he could understand and who could understand him, that the smell of liquor on their breath and the way they slurred their words hardly seemed to matter.

Being drunk and in a good humor, the three were friendly too. When they heard that Wesley had just arrived from Romania and needed a place to stay, they graciously invited him to stay with them.

"For tonight you can stay," they told him. "Its okay, our landlord is away, but only for this one night."

It was a small apartment for four men and one visitor, and the guys talked with each other loudly late into the night. Wesley was tired enough to sleep through it all.

When he awoke, all but one man named Gheorghe had left for work.

Gheorghe grinned amiably at Wesley. "I am between jobs," he told him. He looked almost happy about the fact. He offered Wesley some breakfast leftovers and then shrugged indifferently when Wesley declined the food. "Do you want to go into town with me?" he asked next. "See the sights of Torino? You can leave your luggage here."

Wesley quickly agreed. As soon as he located a public phone he dialed the number of the library where his sister worked.

Iulia – Wesley's sister

"Iulia? It's me, Wesley."

On the other end of the line Wesley heard Iulia gasp. "You are safe?"

"I'm in Torino. In Italy," Wesley told her. Briefly he told his sister about the trip. He made her laugh as he described the suspicious looking border guards, as he talked about the confusion of the train station in Milan. Then he asked her, "How is Mama?" He knew his leaving had been hard on his mother.

"She's fine," Iulia answered.

Wesley pressed the receiver tight against his ear as a short silence built up.

"She's been doing a lot of cooking since you left. It's too much food for the three of us," Iulia laughed and the high musical notes of the sound pierced through Wesley making moisture leak from his eyes. "I miss you already, little brother," Iulia said.

Wesley couldn't respond. He pressed his forehead into his knuckles until they hurt his brow. His coins were running out and he couldn't talk much longer, but it was difficult to break the connection. His sister's voice sounded so comforting, a link with home and familiar things. Around him the city hummed with a strange language and he was more alone than he had ever been in his life.

Chapter 10

No Work, No Money, No Bed

Wesley stayed with Gheorghe and his three roommates for another three days. He knew he was overstaying his welcome, but he had nowhere to go. He didn't know what to do or where to start when it came to beginning a new life in such a strange place.

Every day he walked back to the room full of telephones in the train station to phone his sister in Romania. The familiar sound of her voice was his only comfort in this foreign land for in the bustle of so much unfamiliarity he felt lost. A desperate homesickness choked off many of his words as soon as Iulia began to speak, but he called anyway. He craved the tie with the life he'd left, needing Iulia's soothing voice to tell him what had been happening at home to tell him that he would be all right, that he would soon find work and friends.

On the fourth day that Wesley called Iulia, his sister had some good news.

"I spoke with Simon Ivascu's uncle," she said. "He came into the library. He just walked in while I was on the phone with you last time. I told him that you were in Torino, and that you were discouraged, finding it all so strange. I said you had nowhere to go and didn't know anyone". Her voice trailed off as if she were waiting for Wesley to protest. Then she added, "But it was good I told him because he let me know where Simon lives. He even gave me his phone number there."

Wesley held his breath. A flicker of hope sprang up, warming him.

Iulia's voice grew even softer, as if someone might be listening. "He told me not to tell anyone that he gave out the number."

Wesley nodded. He understood the need to be discreet in such things. If Simon did not yet have legal status in Italy, discretion would be wise. Removing his warm gloves, Wesley wrote down the number Iulia gave him and then he smiled. He wasn't looking forward to making his way back to Milan, and through that maze of trains, in order to get to the town where Simon lived, but it would be a small price to pay to find a friend, a fellow believer who could help him get started in Italy. "I will leave for Milan today," Wesley told Iulia. "I'll phone him as soon as I get there."

"No!" Iulia shouted, almost scaring him. "No. Wesley, he is no longer in Como. Simon is living with his brother in Torino."

Wesley could not believe his good luck and called the number Iulia had given him as soon as he had said good–bye.

Simon sounded a bit odd on the phone. His voice held back, full of suspicion. "Who did you say you were?' he asked.

"Vasile. It's Vasile Pop." In the background Wesley could hear the sounds of construction as Simon was probably in the middle of work. Perhaps he could not hear his voice very well. "I'm from the Viseu De Jos! Not too far from where you live!"

But Simon still seemed wary. Did he think it was a trick, Wesley wondered? Or did he just not recognize him? If Wesley hadn't recognized Simon's voice he might have worried that he had somehow contacted a different Simon, not the one he knew.

"We sang together," Wesley continued. The line grew quiet between them and Wesley worried that Simon might hang up. Desperately he tried again. "You and I rode in that little Dacia all the way to Somcuta, near Baia Mare for evangelistic meetings every weekend when we were younger. We were squished in with another five guys for three hours just to get there. Do you remember? We sang that song, "Because He Lives"? Wesley glanced around to see who might be watching him speak on the phone. Then he began singing, "A song we sing, a song like no other. Yes the day is coming soon when all our hopes will be realized because he lives . . ." Wesley's voice faded away. Then he added, "There were hundreds of people and you were afraid to get on that stage at first." Wesley waited again, searching his mind for other things that might trigger Simon's memory and ease his suspicions.

The song seemed to have convinced Simon for finally his memory returned, or maybe he just began to believe that Wesley was who he said he was. Simon told Wesley that he would meet him in a few hours at the train station when he finished work for the day, and Wesley sighed with relief.

He arrived at the train station early, determined not to miss connecting with Simon. He knew Simon would probably not be there for some time yet. It was too early to begin scanning the crowds of people, looking for him, but Wesley found himself looking anyway.

It had been several years since he had seen Simon. He wasn't altogether sure that he would recognize him anymore or if Simon would know him, and he searched the faces moving past with a new urgency. The station vibrated with the usual bustle of noise and hurry. And there were so many people! It would be easy to overlook one. Wesley settled against a corner wall and watched the people coming into the station from the street.

A loud argument between two men had captured Wesley's attention more than an hour later, and he was intent on watching a policeman intercept the shouting pair when Simon suddenly appeared right in front of Wesley.

For a moment Simon just stood there, studying Wesley. Then he grinned. The smile seemed to set loose a torrent of words from Wesley. It was like breaking a dam as if Wesley had been only waiting for permission to free words that had been imprisoned there. Simon spoke almost as fast, as there was so much to talk about. Simon wanted to hear all the news from home and Wesley asked for advice about finding work and surviving in Italy.

Together, they went back to the apartment where Wesley had been sleeping. There was no one home to offer his thanks or say farewells to so he wrote a quick note instead. Then he collected his suitcase of clothes and took a last look around at the empty bottles and the remnants of last night's party. He wasn't sorry to be leaving.

Outside Wesley watched as Simon glanced around at street names and then confidently announced what bus number they should look for to get across town to where he lived with his brother. He warned Wesley not to speak Romanian while traveling on the bus and gave him a few instructions about how to act. For the first time in many days Wesley felt like he could relax. Simon knew his way around the big city and he knew what to do. He'd found work, and a place to stay. Wesley could learn how to live here if he listened to Simon.

At Simon and Stefan's apartment, conversation continued and Wesley felt optimism grow as he listened to Simon and his brother talk. Life here in Italy suddenly had possibilities. The fear of arrest would never leave any of them, but Wesley felt encouraged knowing that his friend had survived here for almost two years now.

Wesley knew that he could not stay at Simon's apartment, however. The brothers assured him that it would be alright to stay for a day or two if they were careful to keep Wesley's presence unknown to the landlord, but they could not offer much more.

Like many landlords, the man who managed Stefan and Simon's building checked in on them regularly. The man was suspicious of everyone and everything and continually warned them about inviting friends over or even standing around outside the apartment talking with friends.

"It's bad enough that I let you stay here," he often told Simon. "You have no papers. I could get in trouble. You bring friends here, a neighbor hears you speaking Romanian or suspects something, and it all comes back to me," he said, waving his arms around dramatically. Simon explained the landlord's situation to Wesley. Then he said, "It will be okay. Sleep here tonight and tomorrow night. Then you can go to church with us." He shrugged and smiled. "Perhaps at church you will meet someone who knows of work or has a place for you to stay."

Talk drifted to the people they knew from Romania who now lived here and who attended the church in Torino. Soon Stefan was suggesting that Wesley sing with them on the weekend. The brothers were often asked to sing special music, and they welcomed the chance to turn their duet into a trio.

Unfortunately, church didn't produce any help with work or accommodations. Friendly faces smiled encouragements, but shoulders shrugged and heads shook at questions of work.

It was the same over the next week. Wesley met up with many Romanians, but like him, they were looking for work, too. Often Wesley teamed up with them, asking for jobs, sharing leads, offering cautions and standing in food lines together. The small amount of money that Wesley had after he paid for the visa had run very low.

Jobs were scarce in Italy, and every soup kitchen and church food distribution area had long lines of hungry people. Sometimes Wesley would shuffle hopefully along in a seemingly endless line waiting for a hand out of food, only to be turned away when the food ran out before he reached the counters.

On weekends Wesley would sneak back to stay with Simon, Stefan and their roommate, glad for a chance to have a shower and clean up before attending church. Other nights Wesley managed to get a bed at a church or a homeless shelter run by the Red Cross.

There were line-ups for these spots, too, and a limit on how many nights you could stay at such places. So along with others who were just as destitute as he, Wesley often found himself in abandoned houses and in empty boxcars.

While not as cold in Italy as it had been in Romania, it was still winter weather and Wesley sometimes shivered through the hours of the night, hugging a filthy blanket around his shoulders to stay warm, and praying for morning. An assortment of dirty mattresses and a few blankets stiff with dirt were usually all that could be found in the places Wesley found shelter. And always there was the fear of getting caught.

Police didn't come to the shelters or the churches asking for ID, but they were diligent about checking people who loitered on street corners, at the train station, walking along train tracks or in or out of boxcars or abandoned houses. Daily there were whispered reports of this or that person who had been caught. Rumors flew about what happened to such people. Some said prison or deportation. Others described worse fates. Wesley only knew that those who were taken by police never returned to tell their tales.

At night Wesley would feel his heart jump fitfully as he lay awake listening to approaching footsteps. Fear stalked him; it shadowed his footsteps during the daylight hours and crept closer at night, an unwelcome presence in his dreams.

When he and a few others would sneak into an empty boxcar for the night, Wesley's nerves rang, taut with anxiety as he helped slide the heavy door shut with a clang and then waited, hoping no one had heard or reported them.

On Christmas day, December 25, 1998, Wesley was fortunate to get a sagging cot for the night in a church basement.

Along with a roomful of men, he sat listening to Christmas carols on a portable cassette player. In his hands he clutched the bag of fruit and candy each of them had been given. He was lucky, he told himself. It was almost warm enough in this basement room. The kindest thing he could say about the meal he had received was that it had been filling, but it did feel good to have his stomach pleasantly full. And in his hands he held a treasure, a generous handful of nuts and sweets and a whole orange.

Lucky wasn't how he felt though.

"Silent Night, Holy Night, all is calm..." sang out the choir in Italian, and Wesley blinked at the ceiling in an attempt to keep his tears from spilling over. Instead of remembering the Christmas when he had sung "Silent Night" with his brother and sisters he traced the pipes criss–crossing the low basement. He set his thoughts to wondering about the odd yellow paint that had been used to coat the ceiling in an effort to keep from picturing the hearth at his home where his family might be gathered. To distract himself from imagining the Christmas cake his mother would have set out on the cutting board, he set his mind on the task of wondering how a person would go about repainting such a maze of pipe work. Would a painter build some sort of scaffolding, or simply move a ladder about? Were the tops of all those pipes painted the same sick yellow color? Who decided to choose such a color? And would the task of repainting ever be required? Engrossing as such thoughts were, though, they didn't reduce his homesick feelings.

He didn't risk phoning as often any more. He knew now that using a public phone could be dangerous for anyone speaking a different language. The room at the train station that was filled with telephones for public use especially was a place that foreigners were often stopped and questioned by the police.

He had phoned to his family to say Merry Christmas. Wesley didn't tell Iulia much about his life on the streets of Italy, but he suspected she knew life hadn't been easy for him.

"We're praying for you," she'd told him.

113

Remembering her words caused something to turn over in Wesley's stomach with an ache so enormous that for a moment he could hardly catch his breath. He gave up distracting himself with thoughts of yellow paint and thoughts of his home. His family would be seated by the fire. His father would be reading aloud from the Bible. There would be a plate of his mother's Christmas cookies close by.

Were they thinking about him at home? Were they missing him as much as he missed them? What would they think if they could see him now and know what his life had become?

Chapter 11

Caught!

It was near the end of January; during an evangelistic series when Wesley told Simon he wanted to given his heart to God.

An evangelist spoke via satellite every evening at the Torino church, and Wesley and Simon had tried to attend every meeting. After one Friday night meeting Wesley crept into Simon's apartment quite late, having made arrangements to spend the night. Simon and Stefan's roommate already snored loudly from the other room. Stefan was warming something to eat on the stove and Wesley sat down across from Simon and made his announcement.

"I think I will ask for baptism," Wesley said. "When they have an altar call next time, I will go up." Wesley paused when Simon looked up from where he'd been idly sorting out a new tune on the keyboard he and Stefan had bought. "I've been thinking about it for some time now," Wesley added. "I've given my heart to God. I want to be baptized. I may not have another chance. My life is so uncertain now." Wesley shrugged and let his gaze move over the little apartment. "The future does not look that good for me, Simon. You at least have a job here, but you are illegal too. Either one of us could be caught anytime and we would be put in prison." Wesley shook his head and then stood up to begin pacing. "Yesterday all those people were rounded up at the train station. Sent to the police. Sent home, to prison..." Wesley's arms went up into the air, to make an exclamation point. "That one who ran was shot! It could have been me. It can happen that fast."

Simon was nodding.

"We don't know what is going to happen to us," Wesley said. It was almost a whisper. "I want to be baptized. I want to do it while I have this chance. While I am free to do such a thing."

Simon turned off the keyboard and stood to face Wesley. "I've been thinking about baptism too," Simon answered. "I'm ready." Wesley stopped pacing and stared at the serious look on Simon's face.

Young people in Romania usually waited until they were almost adults to make a decision for baptism. Most young men postponed baptism until they had finished the military ordeal. They left off making such an important spiritual commitment until after their term of duty as if military service were some kind of test. If they survived serving in the army with their faith intact, baptism could be considered.

Simon seemed to be reading Wesley's mind. "We can't really ask to be baptized in prison," he said. The words sounded almost joking, but Simon's eyes were solemn as he thought "I can't put God on hold!"

**Simon, Wesley
and friends**

**Romanian choir
in Torino, Italy**

On the day set aside for baptism, every seat was filled. A few other young people and one or two older men stood up in front of the congregation with Simon and Wesley to pledge their lives to God in a beautiful church in Torino. The voices of the Romanian choir filled the building and just before the baptism, Stefan, Simon and Wesley sang special music. Wesley and Simon were barefoot, cloaked in long white baptismal robes as they offered up their song of praise.

Stefan, Wesley, Simon

Simon getting baptized

One Bible, verse directed in turn to each of those who had been baptized, offered words of encouragement for their new lives in Christ.

A long line of smiling faces waited to welcome them. Simon rolled his eyes at Wesley with a conspiratorial smile. More kissing, his look seemed to say. Although greetings of a kiss were also common in Romania, in Italy the habit of kissing felt a little more intense and overwhelming at times. Wesley laughed and bravely went ahead into the waiting church family of well wishers. Every one, man and woman alike, reached out to offer their words of joy, and to kiss him, turning his face in their hands to reach both cheeks.

Tiny Grandma Amalia, who always slipped Wesley and Simon some kind of sweets when she greeted them each weekend, grinned and chuckled as Wesley hugged her lifting her up off the floor in gratitude. Today, instead of a caramel candy, she had flowers to give out. There were flowers for all those who had been baptized. Food, too. A wonderful potluck dinner was laid out, with everyone talking loudly and grinning with happiness.

Wesley caught Simon's eyes across the table where he sat wedged between Grandma Amalia, and Clorinda, a pretty Italian girl who kept blushing when she looked at Simon. There was no space in the noise around them to have his words be heard, so he simply smiled and nodded. Simon smiled back at him and Wesley knew that his friend was just as happy as he was. Like Wesley, Simon had publicly said "yes" to the faith of his childhood that he cherished. He'd given his heart to his God. The world, for this moment felt right and good, and Wesley knew that nothing else before or after this event would ever be as important.

Wesley's world outside of church did not improve and if anything the situation seemed to be getting worse. Everyday there seemed to be more foreigners, more hungry people, more people walking the streets looking for work, more crime. There were drifters from Romania, Albania, and Morocco.

Many of those who had come to the country illegally and failed to find work were becoming desperate. Some had resorted to violent crimes giving a bad name to all the homeless on the streets of Italy. More and more often there was gunfire in the streets now and Italians became openly contemptuous of people like Wesley. They didn't even bother to hide their disgust. Illegal vagrants were spoiling the city, taking jobs, stealing food and possessions, and turning their country into a police state.

When Italians heard people speaking in another language on the bus they would leave their seats and move away, disassociating themselves with the outsiders. It was open prejudice, and it was getting worse all the time.

Wesley hated seeing the looks of disdain thrown his way. He wanted to tell them, "I am not a criminal. I am a nice guy. I am a good person just like you. I just need some kind of work. Just give me a chance to work. I'll do any kind of work." But there was no work. No one wanted to hire someone who did not have the correct papers, and who could barely speak more than a few sentences of Italian.

Wesley spent his days walking, talking to people, looking for leads, and asking those he knew, or had met before, what they had heard.

He folded up the joy he'd felt at his baptism and carried it with him, close to his heart, to take out and warm him with peace when he felt discouraged. He tried to pray and trust that God would intervene somehow, but hope seemed too steep a mountain to climb as he wandered through the streets of Italy, looking for work.

It was late in February when he decided to try something different.

Wesley had grown weary of wandering through the same areas, asking and hoping, but getting the same negative answers about work. When he heard the unmistakable sound of a chain saw in the hills above the city, his ears perked up.

"Emil, listen," he said to the stocky Romanian man who had stood next to him in the line for food that day. "Chain saws. Up there." Wesley pointed. "Maybe there is work for us up there."

Emil frowned and shook his head, squinting in the direction Wesley pointed.

"It's better than looking around here again," Wesley argued. "We could go check it out at least. It doesn't sound like it's too far away."

In moments the two had decided to follow the sound. Their steps were quick for a change, and they both felt hopeful. Wesley anticipated work felling and bucking trees, working with wood high above the stale air of the city streets. Emil surmised that the sound could be from clearing land for a new subdivision in the hills. If they were lucky, he told Wesley, a job like that might keep them in steady work for many weeks.

It wasn't long, however, before Wesley realized the sound had been deceiving. The hum of the chain saws remained constant and far off even after Emil and Wesley had trudged steadily up winding streets for over two hours. The work going on in the bush with chain saws was obviously much farther away than they had originally thought.

Houses began to look different on each subsequently higher level. Streets were wider and some yards were gated. Wesley and Emil began to feel self-consciously out of place.

As they continued walking they realized that they were passing some of the richest looking homes that either of them had ever seen. Expensive cars pulled into covered garages, servants opened grand front entrances. No one was out walking along the manicured lawns and immaculate sidewalks bordering the roads except the two of them.

Wesley didn't want to turn back after they had sweated up this long hill. The hope of real work was too strong, but he began to feel more and more uneasy. Emil too had begun to look tense. The stress in both of them escalated again when they heard police sirens wailing. After a moment they could see the vehicles. There were four, no five police cars hurrying up the winding road towards them.

Nervous as Wesley felt in this upper class neighborhood, he knew his mere presence in this place could not be enough reason for five police cars. The speeding police cars were probably heading to some suspected crime. Perhaps there would be an arrest in one of these mansions. Maybe Emil and Wesley were close to where some drug lord was about to be seized. When the police cars screeched to a stop beside them, Wesley opened his mouth in disbelief.

The police were here for him and Emil!

Fright imprisoned him. Wesley felt the blood drain out of his face. It squeezed out of his heart and puddled somewhere in his knees, making them wobble.

Beside him, Emil's face looked unrecognizable. His whole body seemed taunt, ready to bolt. Wesley put out his hand in an attempt to stay Emil's panic, but it was the wrong movement to make. Instantly three policemen grabbed Wesley. Their quick bursts of words fell around him, sharp as flung rocks. And then he was up against a brick wall being searched for weapons. His ear stung where he'd been pushed into the rough stone.

It was like something from a bad movie, and Wesley was in it.

Chapter 12

Fifteen Days to Get Out!

Wesley knew enough Italian now to understand some of what the police were saying and in a faltering voice he tried to respond. With Emil's stammering help, he attempted to tell the officers that they were not criminals; they were simply looking for a job. They had walked up here following sounds from chain saws, hoping for work. He struggled with the unfamiliar Italian words, feeling them tangle around themselves.

The police were not easily persuaded. In a city full of crime, much of it committed by out of work foreigners, they had become accustomed to being distrustful.

Someone from this expensive neighborhood had probably reported them, Wesley thought. But he was amazed at how roughly the police treated them when they had done nothing wrong. He had no doubt that he and Emil would have been shot if they had decided to run.

Papers and ID were what the police demanded now. And Wesley didn't have any legal ID. Neither did Emil. Wesley's travel visa had run out long ago.

"Where do you live?" the police asked next.

Wesley quickly showed the stern–faced officer the paper that showed that he was presently lodging at a certain downtown shelter. He felt immensely fortunate to be able to tell the police that he was, in fact, registered at a local shelter. Three or four days earlier he would have had to admit that he had nowhere to stay. The shelter wasn't much of course, but an address, even a temporary one, seemed to make some kind of difference.

When the police realized they were simply dealing with two foreign vagrants without legal papers to be in Italy and not armed criminals, all of the police cars except one drove away.

Wesley's heart hammered as the police wrote something out and spoke Italian to each other. Was he to be arrested now? Where would they take him? Would he go to a prison here in Italy? Would he immediately be sent back to Romania? Simon and Stefan and his friends at church would likely never know what had happened to him now.

As one of the police officers approached them with papers in his hands, Wesley prepared his heart to be brave for what lay ahead. "God please give me strength," he breathed. "Let me be a credit to your name."

But the police were letting them go!

Once more, Wesley felt his mouth opening in disbelief. They were free to go. The police gave them each a legal document stating that they must leave the country in 15 days and instructed them very forcibly to leave the area immediately.

Emil looked at Wesley. His black eyes had grown enormous. "I guess we're still free men, my friend," he said quietly.

Wesley nodded. "Guess we'll never find out if there's work up there," he said, scanning the upper hills where the chain saws still whined now and then. He glanced at the policemen in their car and then elbowed Emil. "I think they're waiting for us to get moving."

Going downhill took less energy, but the walk nonetheless was extremely uncomfortable because the police car followed along behind them all the way.

"It would waste less of their day to give us a ride," Emil muttered. His eyes moved sideways to catch another glimpse of the car moving along so slowly behind them.

Both of them were afraid to look back. "Good thing we had shelter addresses to show them," Wesley said. "Or we could be getting a ride right into jail."

Finally the streets began to level out and look familiar, and Wesley and Emil sighed with relief when the police car turned and headed down another street away from them. Sweat coated their faces and their legs trembled from the worry and the quick hike down the steep streets.

Wesley took in a deep breath and stopped to pull out his paper and stare at the Italian words. Fifteen days! How could he possibly leave in 15 days? Where could he go?

The question was unanswerable, but for the next few days Wesley thought of little else. Once more he was contemplating escape. Instead of looking everywhere asking everywhere for work, he began to listen to the talk circulating among other people on the street about ways to leave Italy.

Some of what he heard sounded incredible and very dangerous, but he was beginning to feel desperate enough to listen to all of the ideas he overheard now.

When he crept into Simon and Stefan's apartment late Friday night his head was whirling with new thoughts. He was glad that Simon was still awake.

Simon listened, shaking his head, when Wesley recounted his experience with the police. Then, to Wesley's surprise, Simon told him that he, too, had been stopped by the police that very week. He pulled out his own identical 15 day order and held it up to show Wesley.

Simon and Wesley on the Bus

"My last 15 day permit ran out a year and a half ago," Simon told him. His mouth grinned, but his eyes looked worried. "I'm still in shock that they didn't take me in this time. I think they were just too busy to be bothered with me. So they gave me another one of these." Simon lowered his voice to almost a whisper. "I don't think we can hope for the amnesty that Stefan got a few years ago."

Simon stared down at the police orders in his hand and shook his head. "It's not going to happen for you or me, Wesley."

Wesley agreed with a nod. "I've been hearing things, Simon, about ways to escape. There's been a lot of talk."

"There is always talk," Simon said with a sigh.

Wesley stood up then, smooth as a shadow in the half dark apartment. With careful fluid movements he crossed the floor, opening up a space for his thoughts as he paced out breathing space in the room. He took in a long breath as if he was thirsty for air. Then he asked, "Have you heard about guys escaping in containers?"

"Containers? Boxcars you mean?"

"Like boxcars. Yes." Wesley described their shape with his hands. "Those containers that you see on trucks or on trains. They are sometimes used for smuggling Illegal goods." Wesley let his eyes wander around the little room. "Sometimes guys get into containers here and some of them end up in Australia, or all the way to America. You travel across the ocean on a big container ship."

"Stories," Simon replied.

"No, it's true. This guy, Peter, he gave me a name of a Romanian guy named Rica. He puts guys into containers."

Simon looked up. "For a price of course."

"Yes, a big price. But he gets them out of the country." Wesley stared at Simon, willing him to believe what he told him. The whole idea terrified him. He couldn't imagine deciding to do such a rash thing, but he kept talking anyway. "Some of the ones who left in containers are working in Canada or in the United States right now. Good jobs, too. This one guy had a brother who went over to Montreal. He's working there logging. Good money right away and he didn't even know English."

"Sounds pretty risky."

"I know."

"We'd probably get caught just trying to get near one," Simon said.

Wesley crumpled back down onto the couch and leaned back to close his eyes. "You're probably right," he agreed. "It does sound a bit crazy."

Simon's brother Stefan had even more objections to the idea when he heard them talking about it the next evening. "Don't even think of such things!" he told them. "You get in one of those containers, you die in there. I've heard things too. And everything I've heard is bad. Don't consider such foolishness. You'll find another way."

No other way came along, though, and everyday stress increased for Simon and Wesley. They didn't bring up the subject of escape when they were together, but by the time both of their 15 day permits had expired, they were becoming increasingly anxious.

The two were in the church basement on a Saturday night after an evening service, when Wesley mentioned leaving Italy. He'd been complaining about how difficult it was to find work and mentioned, almost causally, the fact that there were apparently lots of forest industry jobs in North America.

"Guys are earning enough to buy their own trucks in a matter of weeks there," Wesley said. "So I hear," he added. "Can you imagine that kind of money? Just go out and buy a car or a truck after working for less than a month on one job. Amazing!"

"If you can believe it, that is," Wesley added.

Simon stood up, glanced at Wesley and then looked away. "So basically, the only thing that's stopping us from buying one of those nice American trucks is getting ourselves sealed up in a container for a week or so, right?" Simon's voice sounded teasing. Then it changed into something more intense. "We should do it," he said. Abruptly he began pacing, almost bumping his head on a low ceiling beam. "What do you say? Let's do it!"

"What? Get in a container, you mean?" Wesley asked. "Are you serious?" In spite of the warm room, a shiver tingled through his body. Through the high window he could see the thin smile of a moon. Its light barely pierced the black sky. A tickle of hesitation closed up his throat for he hadn't been prepared for such an impulsive statement from Simon. It had all been just talk. Foolishness. The conversation had thudded to a stop, but Wesley's eyes flicked to the stairway anyway, to make sure they were alone.

Silence built up around them. Slowly, Wesley stood to face Simon. His blue eyes darted back and forth, searching Simon's brown ones, trying to gauge his friend's sincerity. His own misgivings made his heart jump painfully in his chest, but there was a new excitement now.

"What if it were possible to reach freedom; a new start?"

Simon met his scrutiny quietly, and then he nodded. "I am serious. I think we should do it," he repeated.

128

Chapter 13

Risky Travel Plans

Both Simon and Wesley agreed that they ought to look into the plan before they made a commitment. They decided they should meet the guy who boasted he could ship them anywhere in a container. They weren't ready to hand over any of Simon's hard–earned money, or their lives until they knew a bit more. And since Simon was working, Wesley traveled down to Genova to meet Rica.

He was excited when he returned to give his report.

"He's a big talker," Wesley admitted. "I think he exaggerates too much. But he seems to know about this container business."

"Do you think we can trust him?" Simon asked.

Wesley shrugged. "The guy is bit odd," he confessed. "He wears these enormous sunglasses everywhere. Strange looking. And he talks so fast." Wesley laughed, remembering Rica's peculiar choice of clothing. His older sister would have described the man as "an interesting character". To Simon, Wesley just said, "He's an illegal from Romania just like us."

"But you think he can do it?" Simon asked. "You think he can get us into a container without us getting caught?"

"I think he can. He's been doing it for awhile now," Wesley answered. "A year now. Maybe two. Some other guy taught him how to get into the containers without breaking the seals, and how to close it again so it doesn't look touched. He sure sounds as if he knows what he is doing. Says he can ship us anywhere we want to go. He watches the papers, figures out when shipments are leaving and for where. Says there are papers posted on the containers to tell you where they are going." Wesley paused, watching Simon's expression. "He wants 1,5 million lire each," he said. (about $2000 Canadian)

Simon frowned and then shrugged.

Wesley continued. "He has this list of things we have to take in with us, how much water to take and what kind of tools we should have along. There were three guys there with him, ready to go that next day. America they said. They're on their way there right now I guess."

Wesley stopped and picked up the glass of water that Simon had put down for him. He didn't tell Simon that the three guys had invited him to go with them. Rica had suggested that there would be lots of room in the container for all four of them. "You can go now," he'd told Wesley. "Go tomorrow with these guys. There is room."

The three escaping Romanians seemed eager to let him come along too.

They'd all be smoking, talking of how much booze they'd have to take along to ride out the high seas, and Wesley did not even consider their offer. He was committed to going with Simon.

Wesley took a long drink of water and then added, "This guy, Rica, acts like it's a sure deal. He comes across like some kind of travel agent or something. He acts like it's just another way to travel." Wesley laughed nervously. "He says there are people who will be waiting for us when we get to the port."

"What do you mean, 'people waiting'?"

"Not police," Wesley interjected. "People to help us. Rica says they come and help us find a place to stay and a job and all that." For a moment Wesley stopped and grinned awkwardly. "I don't know. He claims everyone who he has helped to escape is making so much money, but I don't know if I believe it. I can't believe everything he says." Still, Wesley made a face. His eyebrows lifted. "It sounds okay. Better than I thought."

Simon's face still looked sober, but his head was nodding his agreement.

"The guys who were getting ready to go were all talking about what kind of vehicle they were going to buy when they got to America," Wesley put in as an after thought.

Simon asked, "So we can decide where we want to go?"

"Yes. Anywhere we want," Wesley answered quickly. "Australia or France or India or America, wherever the containers go."

"Not India I hope," Simon exclaimed. "We'd be worse off there than here."

"I told him America," Wesley said. "Canada, too, would be good."

For a moment the air was heavy with thinking. Then abruptly Simon grinned. "Okay then." He took in a deep breath and let a smile spread over his face. "You want to go?" he asked. Without waiting for an answer, he added, "When do we leave?"

Wesley felt his own grin freeze for a moment. The words stalled somewhere in his throat. "We just need the money," he said finally. "We can go as soon as we have the money."

"We should go now then." Simon played the zipper of his jacket up and down and up and down, looking thoughtful. "With my next paycheck there should be enough . . . "

"I will pay you back," Wesley found himself mentioning again. He still didn't know how he felt about Simon paying his way. "As soon as I get working, I'll pay you back."

As before, Simon shrugged off the words. "Don't worry about the money," he said. "I'm not."

That evening the two of them pored over a colorful magazine of American trucks and cars. They drooled over the colorful pictures and picked out which one they would choose, like children with a catalogue of Christmas toys.

Stefan argued with them, spoiling their dreams.

"You can't be thinking straight," he told Simon. "You can't do it. It's suicide!"

Defiantly Simon stood up to his older brother. "We are going, Stefan. We cannot stay here. Do you think we should wait to be deported instead? You see how it is for us now."

"This is not the way!" Stefan insisted.

He disputed the idea vehemently with Simon every chance he got. And sometimes he argued with Simon silently. Wesley wasn't sure how they still managed to keep arguing without words, but he could tell the disagreement continued even when neither brother spoke aloud. He knew they argued about it, too, when he was not there.

Still, Stefan insisted on going along to say good – bye when they boarded the train to Genova, to meet Rica.

It was a silent ride. They had already discussed everything there was to discuss, and there seemed little any of them could think of to say to each other. Each of them battled their own thoughts.

Rica's confident manner helped to relieve the tension somewhat when they arrived at his place. The odd, long-winded man acted like a long lost friend as soon as he established that they did, indeed, have the money to pay him what he asked.

They could not leave immediately, as they had hoped, however. After a careful study of the paper, Rica told them that he would not be able to put them into a container for America until

Sunday night. It was only Thursday when they arrived, and Stefan could not stay through the weekend.

Wesley went to the train station with Simon to see Stefan back on the train to Torino. He stood awkwardly some distance away as Simon said his final good-byes to his brother. He watched as the brothers hugged, and then stood arms length apart, hands resting on each other's shoulders, heads bowed. When his eyes misted, he turned away. He wished he could speak with his family before he left. He'd spoken with his sister, Iulia on the phone several days ago, but he hadn't told her his plans. He'd said only that he probably would not be able to telephone her for a number of weeks. When she'd asked why, Wesley had lied. He'd told her that he had found work out of town. Why worry his family, Wesley thought. He would call them when he was safe in America. He smiled thinking about it. He would be in a new country. Free. He would be finally working. His family would be happy for him.

That day in Genova, Wesley and Simon wandered near a park. Around where they were walking tall palm trees lined the walk, ancient historical landmarks and architectural marvels bore inscriptions and spring blossoms perfumed the air, but they hardly noticed. Their minds were miles away.

The next day, Rica went with them to a big store to buy the supplies they would need. Taking charge like some bossy mother hen, the talkative fellow guided their shopping cart through the aisles as he loaded them up with what he told them they would need. Water first of all. Six heavy bottles of water for each of them; a special type of long lasting bread that Rica insisted on, and some tins of canned fish and beef that could be peeled open. Bars of chocolate and cookies were thrown into the cart as well.

When the food looked sufficient to Rica, they moved on to find the proper tools. Into the cart went a hammer, two chisels, screwdrivers, hacksaw blades for cutting metal, a hand drill with several sizes of bits, cigarette lighters and two plastic flashlights.

Wesley felt a tremor of fear travel along his spine as Rica described to them how they should use the tools when it was safe to get out, or in case they needed more air.

There wasn't much else to pack for personal items. They both had a change of clothing in their packsacks. Wesley had agreed with Simon about leaving all of their identification behind.

"It could be like it was in Italy," Simon explained. "If we get caught with no ID perhaps they won't send us back as quickly."

They both agreed that it had been providential for Simon's ID to have gone missing when it did. If he'd been able to produce his papers when the police had first arrested him in Italy, he would have been immediately shipped back to Romania.

They had both been more worried about getting caught, arrested or deported, than they had been about the dangers of survival inside the container. But now, as they listened to Rica's instructions, Wesley began to worry that getting caught might not be their only concern.

Rica and his helper, Marc, had arranged for a Romanian friend with legal Italian papers, to drive them to the container area. Since Genova was a seaside city, and many ships left from its port harbor, both Wesley and Simon assumed that they would be driven directly down to the docks. But the car headed into the mountains instead. It seemed as if they were heading east, away from the sea, but they made so many turns it was hard to keep a sense of direction. At first, Rica kept up his usual chatter as the VW Golf sped along winding roads and through long dark tunnels, but he wasn't forthcoming about where they were headed. It was all quite mysterious. Wesley got the impression that Rica and Marc did not want him or Simon to know exactly where they were or where they were going. This business provided Rica's income. Perhaps he worried about competition. Maybe he wanted to safeguard the methods he'd developed, and to keep the place where he carried out his clandestine activities a secret.

The silence in the little car grew when Rica ran out of words. Once or twice Wesley caught Simon's eyes, but they didn't speak. Marc sat on the other side of Simon with his forehead resting on the window glass, and Wesley watched out the window on his side while his mind whirled. What were they getting themselves into? Would they even make it to the container without being caught? Could they trust these three men?

Two hours passed before they pulled over and got out of the car. Then, as soon as they had unloaded all their gear and slammed the doors of the car, the expressionless driver drove away leaving them on the side of the road.

"It's not wise to be parked in this area," Rica explained. Then he proceeded to give them a speech about how they must follow his orders very carefully from this point on. All of their lives depended on how well they followed instructions, stayed close and kept quiet.

Twilight had descended by this time. Colors had begun to dissolve into shades of grey and night birds were already calling, but it wasn't dark enough to hide their movements yet. Rica ordered Wesley and Simon to stay hidden, and he and Marc stole into the shadows to look around.

Finally it was time to go.

The four of them strode a short distance along the roadway and then across another street to face an enormous concrete wall.

The region behind the wall was obviously a restricted area that they were not meant to enter. Wesley looked up to see jagged glass embedded into the concrete at the top of the wall and barbed wire loops on top of that. He caught Simon's worried expression and turned as Rica hissed at them both urgently.

"Over here!" Rica gestured to a tree close to the wall. "Up the tree," he told them. "Hurry." His eyes darted around nervously as they all took their turn climbing into the tree. Wesley watched Simon struggle up with his half of the cumbersome load of water, food and tools, grunting as he found footholds in the tree, and then he followed.

"You have to jump over from there," Rica whispered. He pointed to one limb of the tree and made a jumping movement with his hand to show them. "Throw your gear down there first," he said.

It looked like too far a distance to jump down safely, but Simon didn't hesitate. Wesley watched his friend roll as he hit the ground and then looked back up at him, motioning him to hurry. Wesley threw down his gear. Then he held his breath and launched out. He landed with a painful thump bruising one wrist on the gear. Grabbing up his share of the supplies, he hurried after Simon and Marc relieved to see that they had been led into a yard filled with containers.

At last! His stomach felt knotted with anxiety and he longed to just get inside one of the containers and rest away from any authorities that might spot them.

"Here?" he heard Simon ask Rica behind him. "Are these containers here?"

"No," Rica hissed. "We have to walk a ways."

It was quite "a ways" actually. Wesley's arms ached from carrying the supplies, and he felt weary from watching for movement or light and listening for any sound that might indicate watchmen or patrol guards. To the right of them, some distance away, they could hear dogs barking and Marc stopped them twice, to listen.

They crossed an area piled with containers of several sizes, through a field where the uneven dirt caused Marc to curse as he turned an ankle and alongside a railway track littered with parts and pieces of flat cars and boxcars.

**Picture of a railway tracks
and containers**

After about forty–five minutes of walking, Rica barked out an order, and Marc, who was in the lead immediately got down on his belly. Wesley and Simon followed. With grunts, the four of them crawled under a string of boxcars. Sharp rocks stabbed into Wesley's hands and elbows, and he could feel the cold oily underside of the train along his head and back as he pushed himself along. The dogs were barking again. Had they caught their scent? Was that why Rica had made them hide?

Wesley's breath came out in gasps, loud in his ears as it echoed off the metal boxcar above him. The smell of greased machinery filled his lungs. And then there was a light. A patrol car of some kind moved along slowly somewhere on the other side of a parallel set of tracks. The yellow glow from its headlights shone over the ground and under the train causing Wesley to hold his breath for a moment.

They began moving again when Rica gave the signal that all was clear. Cautiously they crept out from under the train and began threading their way through and around railcars and stacked containers again.

They moved among materials waiting to be loaded and some that must have just been shipped in. In spite of being so on edge, Wesley could not help but gasp and stare when they zig zagged through a lot with more light that contained hundreds of expensive German made SUV's. He looked back to catch Simon staring as well. "Which one do you want?" Wesley whispered. Then he grinned and shook his head at the wonder of them. The shiny new vehicles were lined up in orderly rows sporting every color imaginable.

Security was tighter here. Every few moments either Marc or Rica had to motion them all into hiding and stillness when a patrol car moved through the area. Minutes ticked by. It seemed as if they had been walking and hiding for most of the night, but they knew it had been just over two hours. Their hands and shoulders ached with strain when they finally arrived at the right point along the tracks where Rica told them a train would be stopping to load containers for shipment.

Near to where the train was soon to stop, Rica ordered Simon and Wesley to hide inside a culvert under a small bridge.

"Wait here," he told them sternly. "Don't move and don't make a sound."

Marc crouched for a time some distance away, watching. And then he too crept over to the tracks where Rica had gone.

Wesley heard the train arrive almost an hour later. They both slithered out of their hiding spot to watch as Rica hopped up onto a piece of train joining the boxcars, lithe as a tiger in the dark. He drew out a tool from inside his jacket and Wesley could see a watery rippling of light gleam down its shiny surface. Quick as an indrawn breath the man had opened the container. Almost as quickly he'd closed it again. Then he darted around to another.

Rica opened and then closed three containers before the two came back. In the short amount of time while the train sat in this position it was quite a feat to open more than two, Marc told them.

It was just after 5 am, when Rica joined them back in the culvert. "Nothing!" he spat. "No room at all. They were all full of wood. I wouldn't squeeze my dog in that little space." He shook his head angrily. "And there was no time left to look in more."

"So we wait another hour or so for the next train?" Wesley ventured.

"No. There won't be another train moving through here until this time tomorrow," Rica answered. He sounded annoyed. "We have to stay and wait."

Wesley stared, letting his breath out in a long slow sigh. Beside him Simon groaned. Marc scowled sullenly. Wait? All night? And all day tomorrow waiting and hiding? It felt like a lifetime. But there was nothing they could do about it. Reluctantly Wesley and Simon followed Rica and Marc as they led the way to somewhere they could hide safely until Rica could find them a suitable container.

Chapter 14

Inside a Container Box

A spreading line of brighter grey showed at the sky's edge as the four trudged back through an open field and then into an area of empty containers.

Most of the rectangular metal boxes here looked to have been sitting idle for some time, and Rica went confidently to one near the centre of the group. One after another, they hoisted their gear and then themselves up into the empty boxcar and stood looking into the dim interior.

Wesley had spent many nights in boxcars similar to this back in Torino. Those had often contained some type of materials, goods that were being transported, or some make–shift bedding or blankets. This one was echoingly empty and cold. The chill night air outside had been warmer than the air inside.

Marc produced a bottle of plum brandy and waved it at them. "It's good I brought the essentials, eh?" he said. He settled himself down against one wall and lifted the bottle to his lips.

Wesley wasn't even tempted to share the liquor Marc offered.

For awhile, they huddled close together. Rica talked about the shipping schedule, and some of the other groups of escapees that he had successfully sealed into containers. When he began boasting about some of his shady operations, Wesley exchanged anxious looks with Simon. Rica spoke of his time in prison and his criminal exploits in such an offhanded manner that worry snuck into Wesley's mind to squeeze up against the stress already holding his muscles tense. Could they trust this character?

When Rica had run out of stories and decided he wanted to sleep, Marc took over. He entertained them with sea voyage tales from the time when he had crewed several tankers and container ships years ago.

"Wouldn't get me out there again for any wage," he told them. "I spent the whole time chipping rust and patching holes with epoxy." For another hour or so Marc regaled them with stories of foreign ports, crazy commanding officers and stories of storms that sounded too unbelievable to be true.

Wesley decided that the drink was probably contributing to Marc's exaggerated tales. He said very little, himself, but when the opportunity arose, Wesley followed Simon to the other end of the container to lie down and try to get some sleep.

They lay with their heads on the packsacks that held their change of clothing and hugged themselves into balls to keep the small warmth of their bodies from evaporating.

A damp chill began fingering its way through their feet and legs and then gradually enveloped them until they were both shivering.

Wesley felt welcome warmth at his back when Simon pushed his own back against him, but it wasn't enough for comfort.

On the other side of the boxcar Wesley could hear the higher, more strident whispering of Rica again. He was awake. Or perhaps he had never slept. He was attempting to keep his voice hushed, but Wesley could tell he was arguing with Marc. He could hear the tone of their voices well enough to know they were unhappy about something, but he could not make out any of their words.

"Simon, you asleep?" he whispered.

To answer, Simon grunted. Sarcastically he answered, "On this soft bed?"

"Yeah. I think my hip and my shoulder are going to be bruised," Wesley replied. Then he maneuvered onto his back and turned his head to whisper in a quieter voice. "I heard Marc tell our driver that he would see him in a few hours," he said. "I don't think this extra day is in their plans. I know Marc didn't like the idea of staying in here. What if they just wait until we are sleeping and leave us here? They already have our money."

Simon didn't answer right away. Then he asked, "Do you think we should take turns keeping watch?"

"I don't think I'm going to sleep anyway."

The worry and the cold kept Wesley alert long after he heard Simon's even breathing. He couldn't tell if Rica and Marc slept. There was no snoring and they weren't whispering either. If he stayed awake he knew that he would hear the door open should they decide to sneak away.

His ears were straining so intently to hear every sound that he felt surprised to feel suddenly warm. A bright light filtered into his eyes as he shifted position and he lifted his head. He had slept! Simon sat near the door of the boxcar with Marc, peeking out through the crack of light that was hitting Wesley's eyes.

Wesley looked at his watch and groaned. Only 10 am? There were still so many hours to wait. Gradually the pleasant warmth inside their hide out increased until it was anything but pleasant. By mid afternoon the chilling temperatures of the previous night had reversed themselves to stifling heat. The air became thick and Wesley felt his breath clog in his throat. He took his turn with Simon and Marc at the crack in the door trying to get a breath of fresh air.

Time dragged by.

Wesley felt grateful that Rica and Marc had not deserted them and was charitable enough to share out some of the food they had purchased for their journey. But the four didn't attempt any conversation even while they were eating. From the tense lines on their faces, Wesley decided that they each had worries enough to occupy the hours without needing conversation. They'd heard few sounds outside around them, but they knew security in this whole area was tight. If any of them were caught here, they'd be much more than foreigners without ID. They'd be criminals in a restricted area.

The inside of the boxcar was pitch black again and already chilly when Rica led them back to the culvert to wait. Wesley and Marc stood guard, near their gear, and Simon followed Rica across the field to the place where the train would arrive. Wesley stretched his neck to see when he heard the noise of the approaching train. He cringed, as he watched Rica jump up to begin drilling with his cordless drill. Along with Marc he scanned the area repeatedly for any security guards.

Wesley was too far away to see exactly what Rica was doing, but he marveled at how quickly the man moved exchanging a number of different tools as he worked. He opened one container, looked in briefly and then closed it up again. Beside him, Wesley heard Marc sigh.

Wesley was watching for patrol lights back in the direction from which they'd come and wondered if they might get stuck here another night when he saw Simon running back. "Bring the stuff," Simon said. "Rica's found us a container."

At the train, Simon didn't hesitate. He hopped up onto the boxcar coupling and then into the container without even looking back. His hand reached out for their gear as Marc began throwing it to him.

Rica motioned to Wesley. "Get in," he hissed. "Hurry."

The container looked full to Wesley. Cardboard wrapped crates were stacked shoulder high inside, tight against both sides

144

of the container. The space between the doors and the cardboard stacks was only a shoe length wide. Wesley stepped inside and pulled himself up on top of the crates as the last of their gear was thrown in. He jumped at the boom of the door being shut and blinked in surprise at his instant blindness. Darkness hid even their faces from each other. He hadn't even said good–bye to Rica or Marc.

Beside him Simon whispered, "Ceramic tiles. There are several big skids of them."

Wesley nodded. As he straightened his body to sit up straight, his hair brushed the roof of the container. "Is it already starting to move?" he whispered to Simon.

"It's been jiggling around a bit," Simon answered. "I hope it's not leaving yet." Wesley could feel Simon's breath against his ear. "If Rica doesn't get the bolt replaced and everything finished up right . . . well . . . The customs guys will open it up and check it out for sure if anything looks suspicious."

Wesley stared in alarm at the darkness around Simon's voice. "Can you hear the drill?" he asked.

Containers on the train

Simon didn't answer right away. Then he said. "I can't hear anything. Rica will tap on the side two times to let us know when he's finished though. I think we will hear that."

"If the security guys come around before Rica is finished, or if the train starts moving, he'll have to quit," Wesley murmured. He felt his words falter in his mouth and he didn't know if Simon had heard him or not. He didn't want to voice what they both were worrying about. Rica already had their money, and he wasn't likely to risk his own neck for them anymore now. Would he stick by to finish if he suspected a patrol was approaching? If the train began rolling away, would Rica keep working?

A slight movement jarred them both. "It is moving," Wesley said.

Simon didn't answer.

Maybe they would have to jump back out, Wesley thought. If Rica hadn't managed to finish replacing the bolt correctly, it wouldn't be wise to stay inside. But if Rica didn't open the door for them, they couldn't get out. They were trapped in there. Sour bile crept up Wesley's throat, and a bitter taste filled his mouth as if he were breathing in the cold metal taste of the container. Even if the bolt hadn't been completely secured they would not be able to force the doors open from the inside. That's why they had brought tools. They would need to cut a hole big enough for an arm to push through so they could open the outside bolts once they arrived at their destination. But cutting their way out would be a long, hard task. Starting such a job now would be sure to fail. They'd be caught attempting such work here in the shipping yards where patrols circled regularly.

A screeching cacophony of protests arose from the metal railway tracks, and the train lurched again as it started to move.

Then they heard it. The distinct sound of two sharp taps on the side - wall of the container.

"Good man, Rica," Simon breathed.

Wesley could hear the smile in his friend's voice. A sigh of relief pushed out of his mouth. He sat down and changed his grip as the train's movements settled into an even pace and rhythm.

They weren't moving very fast, but they were finally on their way.

"So," Simon breathed, as if the one word could sum up everything they were thinking. "He's gone then," he said. "We're on our own."

"On our own," Wesley echoed. His tense muscles melted down a few inches and his breath returned to slower gasps. "On our way to America."

"I hope so," Simon answered.

In the dark, Wesley couldn't see the expression on Simon's face, but he hadn't liked the tone of Simon's words.

"What do you mean, you hope so?" Wesley asked. In spite of the tick, tick, tick, of the rail noise beneath them, they were both still whispering.

Simon's shoulder brushed Wesley's as he leaned closer. "There was no paper about destination on the door of this container," he said.

Wesley took in the words, trying to digest them. "But, Rica knew we wanted to go to America. Why would he open this one for us if he didn't even know where this container was going? You mean we could be going anywhere?" The tone of Wesley's voice had risen, sounding high and too loud in his ears.

"Rica said probably America," Simon replied.

"Probably?" Wesley stared into the darkness of Simon's face, waiting. But there seemed nothing else to say.

And then the train was stopping again. They had barely adjusted themselves to the movement and the rhythm of the clickety-click, as it was slowing down in jerks and shudders with squealing brakes.

Beside them a vehicle rumbled past them and they waited, holding themselves still to listen. For ten more minutes they waited and listened, and then the train began moving once more.

For another hour or so their dark world moved and stopped and jerked. Rail wheel brakes squealed beneath them, couplings clunked together at every start and stop, and Wesley and Simon sat in the darkness silently, holding to the edges of the cardboard skids to stay upright amid the jolts and lurches.

147

When the train had stayed still and silent for more than ten minutes, Simon whispered, "Do you think we're at the docks? It doesn't feel like we've traveled very far."

Wesley agreed with a nod, even though he knew Simon could not see his head move. It hardly seemed possible that they had gotten close enough to the water for the container ships to load them aboard already.

For a few more moments neither of them spoke. Then Simon offered, "Might be that there are other containers ahead of us on the track that have to move first." His words had shrunk to something less than a whisper in the sudden quiet.

"Shush," Wesley hushed him. In the dark Simon's voice sounded loud and Wesley felt afraid to even whisper back. The clanking of the tracks had stopped to leave a hollow emptiness in his ears.

Time passed, slow as counted breaths. Simon risked turning on a flashlight, covering most of the narrow beam of the small light with his hand as he tried to illuminate his watch.

"Eight o'clock", he announced. "If it's already light outside they won't see the flashlight beam." He didn't sound sure though, and he didn't remove his hand from around the small circle of light.

Wesley squinted upwards trying to search out the ceiling and the unseen corners of their rectangular home. With not even a crack of light showing anywhere, it was hard to believe that a bright new day could be shining outside. Inside it was cold still, with a middle of the night kind of darkness.

Moving in slow motion, careful not to make any noise, Wesley started shifting around the gear, finding a more comfortable position for his legs. Something rustled beneath the water bottles when he pushed them to another spot. Wesley pulled out the folded paper. "Rica's newspaper," he whispered. "He must have thrown it in by mistake."

Simon inched over to hold the light close to the paper. For a moment they both bent over the rows of small print, scanning the lines that were marked. Simon pointed. "That one," he whispered.

Wesley nodded. "Looks like we're going to Canada," he said.

"If we leave today," Simon answered.

Time and silence stretched long around them as they listened. Twice they heard voices outside. One man barking orders and two other men talking together as they walked some distance away.

There were vehicle sounds, too. Most likely some were patrol cars. And then what sounded like a large truck or tractor moved around not far away from them, and a whining kind of machine noise began.

When they spoke, their voices were quieter than a whisper. Waiting grew painful. They didn't know if the train would lurch into motion again at any moment or if it was going to stay here forever.

Surprise startled a hiccup kind of noise from Wesley's throat when something heavy clunked down right on top of their container.

"They're picking us up," he whispered.

It was terribly loud. It felt as if the roof of their container was about to be taken right off. And then they were moving. This time they were rising up into the air.

"Hang on," Simon told him. "We're going up. Hope they don't drop us."

Wesley stared in the direction of Simon's voice. He hadn't worried about anything like being dropped, but now of course he imagined it. It could happen, he thought. What if the giant gantry crane didn't secure a safe hold on both ends of the box . . . ? What if the crane operator swung the container into something by mistake . . . ?

For a second or two he entertained the picture of their box slamming down, splintering apart with heavy ceramic tile skids crushing into them. Then he ordered his mind away from such pictures.

An odd, unpleasant sensation washed through Wesley as the container moved. Without being able to see anything he felt somehow detached from his own body as though he'd suddenly grown dizzy and disoriented. There was no sense of direction that he could determine in the pitch blackness around him. He imagined they would be lifted up, swung over and then lowered onto the container ship deck, but he could not tell if the container was still going up, if it had started down or if the crane now had swung them sideways. He could sense only disorientation and an unexplainable feeling of space around him.

Wesley's empty stomach heaved uncomfortably inside him, taking up a new unwelcome residence near his throat and then it fell against the wall of his heart as their container plunked down hard on the ship's deck.

Chapter 15

Baked Alive

As the box dropped, Simon relaxed his hands from where he'd been gripping the sides of the skids in the container. Relief opened his lungs and let him gasp out a long breath and then draw one in. He hadn't realized that he'd been holding his breath while the crane swung them through the air.

Since they'd clunked down onto the deck of the ship there had been a steady thrum of activity. The crane still whined and clunked, moving containers. Some landed loudly around them. At least two seemed to have been placed on top of them. Voices hollered back and forth to each other. Simon even thought he heard some kind of vehicle chugging by beside them. Once he distinctly heard someone walking beside their container.

In spite of all the noise and activity happening outside, Simon didn't dare even whisper anything to Wesley. What if someone was standing right outside their container and heard them?

After a few moments of listening, Simon heard Wesley taking off his jacket for it was getting very warm. In the smothering blackness around them, Simon could scarcely picture a blazing hot sun.

Following Wesley's lead, Simon removed his own jacket, moving slowly and carefully to keep from making any noise. Wadding his jacket into a pillow he lowered his body down to stretch out his legs.

With the fingers of one hand Simon felt along the cardboard beneath him to the centre of the skid on which he lay. He could feel the hard, colder surface of the ceramic tiles. With his other hand he reached up. The roof of the container was close enough to touch with the tips of his fingers when he stretched his arm straight up, but in the darkness he could see nothing of what it looked like.

He closed his eyes. His ears almost hurt from listening so intently.

Stifling heat awakened him. Sweat ran down his face, and he could feel it wet along his back where he'd been lying. He stayed still, feeling for a rocking of waves or some kind of motion, but the container was still. The ship was probably still in port.

"It's after three o'clock," Wesley whispered. His voice sounded thick with sleep.

Simon groped about for the flashlight to confirm the fact. He had slept so long! He hadn't thought he would be able to relax with such a lot of noise outside, but his body's need for sleep had taken over. Exhaustion had claimed both of them in spite of the noise.

Containers in the port

"Feels like an oven in here," Wesley complained.

Simon listened to the sounds of Wesley sitting up to peel off his shirt. He lay there while Wesley began fumbling through the food bags and then sat up to pull off his own shirt. Even an undershirt felt like too much clothing in the close heat around them and Simon thought of the boxcar they'd slept in the previous night. When that container had grown too close and hot inside they had cracked open the door for some fresh air and the welcome brush of a breeze from outside. Here they had no such option.

His eyes seemed to be adjusting to the dimness now. He could just make out Wesley's cross-legged shape, across from him.

"It's taking a long time for them to load, isn't it?" Wesley whispered.

Simon started to answer and then stopped himself. He didn't want to voice the doubts he was beginning to feel about where they were. If he kept his misgivings to himself, perhaps they would not become true.

They shared a small can of meat in silence, stopping mid chew whenever they heard something close by. Simon tore off a portion of the strange long-lasting bread Rica had insisted that

153

they buy. It was almost inedible. "This bread is awful," he told Wesley.

Wesley reached over and tore off a chunk of the spongy stuff and put it into his mouth. "Ugghh!" he exclaimed. "Disgusting."

Simon rewrapped the bread and picked up the water bottle. The heat had stolen his appetite anyway, and he was more thirsty than hungry.

He was on his second gulp of water when Wesley reached out a hand in warning.

Instantly Simon stifled the noise of the water bottle and froze to alertness. There were voices right outside the back doors of their container. Then a bumping began against the door itself. A bang against the metal sounded, and someone seemed to be fiddling with the bolt on the door. A shot of adrenaline raced through Simon.

"They're opening the door," Wesley whispered. His voice was so soft it was barely audible; more like air moving by his ear than sound.

Simon shushed him anyway. He felt sick with fear. If the doors were opened they would be found and arrested. There was nowhere to run. Nothing they could do.

Barely breathing, they waited and listened. When the noises on their door stopped neither of them relaxed for several moments. Why had someone been fiddling with the door? Had they changed their mind about looking inside? Had they gone seeking a tool to work the bolt? Had they even been trying to open the door? But what else would they be doing back there?

After some time, Simon let his other worry push against his thoughts as he listened to the sounds from outside the container.

"Maybe we're not even on a ship," he finally ventured.

Wesley didn't respond, but Simon could tell he was listening. His body had grown still.

Simon leaned closer to his friend to whisper, "There's a car or a truck or something driving around out there. It sounds like that patrol truck we saw before."

"There could be vehicles moving around on the ship," Wesley offered. "Container ships, you know they're huge. And if they're still loading . . . well . . ." his voice broke away, unsure.

Simon shook his head back and forth while he thought about it. He wanted to believe they were on the ship but the noises outside argued with his wishes. Somehow he didn't think a ship could afford to sit in port this long. Time was money for these guys. Hadn't Marc boasted about how fast a container ship could dock and load and be underway again in a matter of hours?

It was too hot to do anything more than lie still, and as the afternoon wore on they even stopped whispering to each other.

Machinery had quieted, voices had disappeared and the heat in their container began to leach away when their rumbling stomachs alerted them of hunger once more. But shortly after the evening's welcome, coolness seeped inside to replace the oppressive heat they'd endured, it grew almost too cold again. Simon did up his jacket, scooped corned beef from a little can and tried another mouthful or two of the awful bread. Then he settled down, hoping for sleep.

When a rumble of activity and vehicles and voices began once more the next morning, the very same kind of noise and activity they had heard the day before, both Simon and Wesley admitted the sad truth. They were not on board a ship; they were still on land. They were likely in a large shipping yard, close to the docks.

There seemed to be no point in speaking about it.

They were afraid to make any noise anyway. Even though machinery noises over shadowed their voices and it felt as if the busy outside activities were loud enough to drown out their own small paper rattling or water swallowing, it only took a pair of running footsteps beside them or a quick startling shout close by

155

to keep them cautious. There were people out there. They heard workmen, security officers and patrols.

Once more noises were heard at their door. Once more their dark world began to grow too warm for comfort. Simon itched with a restlessness he couldn't scratch. He felt frustrated with the idle waiting and the frightening uncertainty. Another day holding still, staying quiet and wondering. Another day of enduring the stifling heat of the metal container. Suddenly it felt impossible to endure.

Something had obviously gone very wrong with the plan. Rica had told them that they would be loaded onto a ship, heading out to sea by yesterday noon. At no time did he even mention that their crate might sit around in a shipping yard for a time before being loaded for the sea passage. Rolling to his stomach, Simon smothered the entire small plastic flashlight in his right fist, cupping its light with his left hand and aiming its beam down on Rica's newspaper. He could only hope that today would be the day their container would be loaded aboard a ship, and they would still be okay if they were loaded today. They might have to drink less water, and they might end up in Australia instead of America, but it could still work.

Wesley leaned closer, looking at the schedule on Rica's paper. "Anywhere except India," he whispered.

They hadn't spoken to each other for so long that Wesley's voice took Simon by surprise. He shook his head and grinned back at Wesley in the darkness. Both of them had heard horrific stories of people getting caught in India. Rumor had it that immigrants caught as stowaways were imprisoned and then enslaved, forced to work off any number of expenses or offences.

"Nothing leaving for India until Saturday," Simon told Wesley.

"We'll be two portions of well−cooked meat by Saturday," Wesley whispered back. He struggled up to a crouching position and then started a measured crawl to the edge of the larger skid of tiles to the back doors they had entered by. Simon heard his quick sharp intake of breath when Wesley's skin accidentally touched the burning hot metal of the container.

There were only two places near the front and the back of the container where they could manage to squeeze down and stand up on the floor. They'd designated the back for their waste area using a garbage bag they could tie and their empty water bottles when they had to relieve themselves.

Simon wiped the sweat from his face and then laid his forehead down on one arm.

It was early still, not even noon, and already it was much hotter than it had been yesterday in their metal hide out. The air was too hot to breathe properly and even the drinking water felt too warm to drink.

Pushing away the despair that threatened to overwhelm him, Simon sent words of supplication heavenward. Without God's intervention, he knew they didn't have much chance of escaping, or even surviving.

Both of them managed to sleep a little. It wasn't a very deep or a very restful sleep and they both jumped when they heard something drop on the roof of their container.

Simon sat right up and stared at the black roof. It sounded as if someone were throwing pieces of gravel down on their container.

"Rain?" Wesley asked.

Simon smiled. It was rain. In moments the flung gravel sounds changed to a more rhythmic pling and splat kind of noise. There were some enormous drops; and then it turned into a deafening roar as the huge drops came down in clusters, ringing out a song on the metal roof.

In moments the insufferable heat had dissipated with the roar of noise and breathing became easier. Beside him, Wesley whispered, "I was getting ready to find those hack saw blades. I felt as if we were being cooked alive."

Simon could barely hear him over the water sounds, but he shushed him anyway. He wasn't sure if their voices would carry over the din of noise, but he didn't suspect the din would be as loud for someone walking by outside either.

The words Wesley had just spoken, 'being cooked alive', brought back one of the conversations he'd had with Stefan over a week ago now. Refugees seeking asylum from China had died in a container like this one. They'd paid enormous sums to gangsters called "Snakeheads", desperate to find a better life. They had all found death instead. Stefan had told Simon that the medical team who examined the bodies reported oxygen deprivation and heat to be the cause of death. They'd suffocated while they'd been baked alive.

Simon shivered. In spite of the welcome rain he felt uneasy and then sluggish with disappointment by the time the workday sounds around them ceased. They were still not on a ship, but in the shipyard. "It's Wednesday evening," he announced to no one in particular.

Wesley elbowed over to whisper, "Are you thinking we should try to cut our way out of here?" he asked.

"No," Simon replied. But for most of the day that had been exactly what he had been thinking. It was crazy to consider. Cutting a hole in the container would take some time and make a lot of noise. Here in a high security area of the shipping yard they would almost certainly be caught and dealt with very severely. Besides being illegal, criminal charges would be laid against them this time for breaking into a restricted shipping area. Sawing their way out now was ludicrous, but the thought of spending another day trapped in this container, going nowhere, hardly seemed a better fate.

They were both still awake after ten o'clock. Neither felt sleepy, and it was quiet outside now. Only the occasional sound of a patrol vehicle circling the yard broke the silence. Simon knew that there could also be a security person wandering the lot on foot so they kept their whispering hushed and listened carefully in between speaking.

They bravely spoke of the distinct possibility that their container would not be loaded aboard a ship any time soon. For all they knew it could sit in this spot in the shipyard for weeks. Longer maybe.

They might have to cut their way out. According to Rica, an arm–sized hole should be cut within reach of the heavy outside bolts on the door. Once they could get an arm outside and bend an elbow they would be able to push out the levers turning the bolts free of their locks top and bottom. Only then could they push open the doors.

"It should work," Simon assured Wesley. "What Rica told us; I mean. He was good. I think he really knew what he was doing, you know?" Simon shook his head, remembering how amazed he'd been as he'd watched the man work. "I watched him opening and closing the containers, and I could hardly believe how fast he moved with all those different tools. He had it all down to the minute. Sliced through that bolt, used his drill to thread a closing bolt inside, wiped off all those metal shavings and even brushed off prints and took time to throw dust back onto the handles when he was done." Simon felt his own hands moving to explain how Rica worked even though he realized that Wesley couldn't see him in the darkness. After a moment of thinking he added, "Watching that, well, it makes me think he knew what he was talking about. He must have figured out the system that would work to open it from inside."

"Not that he was ever inside having to get out," Wesley whispered.

Simon didn't answer. He lay there battling the debate. Should they use this time to work at breaking out of their self–inflicted prison? Would they have a chance of running through the shadows to safety under the cover of dark? Or should they wait? Perhaps tomorrow they would be loaded onto a ship. Or perhaps tomorrow they'd lie helpless, struggling to breathe while the container heated up to unbearable temperatures.

As awful as conditions in this metal box had been the last two days, Simon still felt less afraid of suffering than afraid of being captured.

Chapter 16

Running out of Oxygen!

In his dream, Simon swept the new wooden floor of a construction site. His arm ached from the effort. Below him, two floors down, his boss was yelling at someone. When he managed to struggle up into wakefulness, the yelling seemed to come with him, coming from outside the container. The slow swish, swish sounds of the broom continued too, even as his eyes opened.

Grimacing, Simon unfolded his arm from where it had been squished against his flashlight and propped himself up on one elbow. Workmen outside were hollering at each other in Italian. The sweeping broom sound was coming from Wesley. Simon held his own breath to listen to the odd, shallow rhythm of it. It didn't sound right. Wesley wasn't breathing normally.

"Wake up," Simon hissed to Wesley. "Hey, wake up. You're having a bad dream."

Wesley didn't remember a dream, though. His breathing didn't seem to improve much after he was fully awake either.

Simon held the bottle of water out to his friend and listened as Wesley gulped down the warm liquid.

The shade of darkness hadn't changed any, but Simon knew the sun must have been beating down on them again. As the container gradually began to heat up he found his own breathing become more labored. It felt as though he couldn't take in enough of the thick hot air to satisfy his lungs.

They passed the time listening to the sounds in the shipyard around them, speaking and moving less and less as the heat became more oppressive. There was little point in speculating to each other when, or if, they might get loaded onto a ship. Concerns about how much water they were going through seemed a useless topic of conversation. Making any noise still felt too risky anyway, and it took too much effort to whisper to each other. Simon found himself thinking that perhaps they should have chanced trying to get out the night before when he'd felt stronger.

Hours passed, crawling. Simon no longer bothered to shine his flashlight on his watch. It seemed pointless to know the time. When he thought about it very long, Simon wasn't even sure he remembered what day it was. He couldn't remember when they'd first gotten into the container or how much time had passed since they'd been lifted off the train. His mind felt fuzzy and slow.

Neither of them felt like eating much, but they kept drinking. Simon knew they should be rationing their water, but that, too, felt like something that would take more effort than he could muster.

Once more a storm of rain saved them. Just as the heat became unbearable drumming raindrops splattered down to cool the burning hot walls of their prison and make the air less stifling. Even when the air felt cooler, though, it still seemed to be hard to breath. Simon closed his eyes and waited for the welcome drop in temperatures as he listened to the water hitting their roof. Grateful as he was for the rain, Simon wished for other roof sounds. He longed to hear the sounds of a crane and the clunk of metal on metal that would tell them they were being moved onto a ship.

162

But nothing sounded on the roof of their container the next day either. Nothing except rain. By the time the rain had tapered off and the workmen had gone home, Simon felt discouragement weighing him down like an illness.

He turned off the flashlight he'd used to traverse the length of their container on his way back to their sleeping area and faced Wesley. For several moments he groped to find words for his thoughts. Finally he gave up and said, "I think we're in trouble."

"I think you're right," Wesley whispered back.

And then there didn't seem to be anything else to say.

A few hours later, when they began speaking again, neither of them mentioned their dire situation. Instead they talked about their families, a fact that seemed to emphasize their bleak future.

"It's Friday, isn't it?" Wesley asked. Without waiting for Simon to answer he said. "I loved being home every weekend. My mom and my sister would usually spend lots of time in the kitchen. And the smells of all their cooking and baking, before every weekend . . ." Wesley took in a deep breath as if he could actually smell the warm bread on the counter.

Simon's own breath snagged in his throat, remembering his home. When it felt safe to speak he said, "The house would be spotless. I remember I always felt excited, you know?" And the food... O boy, the food!

"I know," Wesley agreed. His voice had grown eager with longing. In spite of the happy lift in his voice, Wesley had to pause. It sounded as if he were having trouble breathing again, as if he were out of breath after running. "I'd always go through the kitchen for something, trying to sneak tastes, or grab a cookie. Mam or Iulia would scold me..."

Simon listened as Wesley's whispered memories petered out, and then waited some more to see if Wesley were finished speaking. Then he said, "My mother made these cookies with raisins and sometimes nuts too. They were soooo good! I could tell by the smell of the house when I first walked in if she had made them that Friday."

Remembering grabbed Simon so strongly that he could almost smell the sweet warmth of his mother's kitchen. His eyes stung as he pictured the way his mother dashed back and forth between the stove and the table, trying to do several tasks at once. Sorrow gathered into him from every hidden corner of blackness, pressing against his chest.

"Do you want to open the cookies?" Wesley asked.

"If you want to," Simon answered. They'd eaten the chocolate on their second afternoon in the container and it had been a mess of melted goo. But for some reason, they hadn't wanted to open the cookies, thinking to save them back as a treat. They would be a poor substitution for the home made cookies their mothers made every weekend, but Simon had still been looking forward to opening the bag. However, for a few more minutes Simon sat staring at nothing, listening to the odd breathing style that Wesley had developed in the last day or so.

To distract himself from his thoughts he pushed himself up into a cross-legged sitting position and grabbed up the sports bag that carried his extra clothing. A few days ago he'd decided the nylon sleeves around the handles might perform well as a secret spot for his money. Now, with their captured feeling more and more certain, he thought he might as well carry out his plan to hide away his cash. The Italian lire he had left didn't amount to any significant sum, but he didn't want the authorities to confiscate all his money like they had the last time he was caught. In the flashlight's circle of illumination, Simon began working at one end of the sock-like nylon sleeve on one handle of his bag. He had to cut the threads, but he felt pleased with the final result.

He fished around for one of the little cigarette lighters they'd brought along, planning to use the flame to melt the nylon edges closed. But the lighter didn't seem to work. Flicking it aside, Simon felt around for the other one. He felt irritated and strangely out of breath by the time he found it. But that lighter would not light either. Over and over again he tried to get the thing to catch, but there was not even a flicker. He could feel the weight of butane in the small cylinder when he shook it. He could even smell the fuel as he worked the tiny gear, but no flame burst up.

Frustration turned into exasperation. Why wouldn't the silly things work? He and Wesley had tested them just days ago as they'd packed. Both had been working fine. With reluctance, Simon allowed the niggling fingers of a distant worry to creep in closer. With effort he gave his sluggish brain permission to consider something almost too horrifying to believe.

They were running out of oxygen. The container was airtight. They had never seen so much as a crack of light even in the brilliant daylight because every corner was sealed tight. Wesley wasn't breathing right because the supply of breathable air had grown dangerously low. His own thinking felt slow and confusing because of oxygen deprivation. The lighter would not light because the oxygen levels were too thin. The stagnant fetid air in their box was turning into carbon dioxide.

A whoosh of panic shot up Simon's spine and prickled his scalp flushing his brain of all rational thought. They were suffocating! Every breath he exhaled added to the poison.

Beside him Wesley was sitting up, whispering questions. His words sounded somehow urgent, but Simon wasn't listening. He'd given in to the insanity of his fear. Suddenly Simon couldn't catch his breath for there was no air to take in.

"We're running out of air," he told Wesley. "We're running out of air." He couldn't tell if he was whispering or yelling. A hollow ringing had begun in his eardrums as with fumbling fingers he groped through the tools they'd hauled in with them.

He used their knife in his first desperate attempt to reach some outside air. Gouging frantically at the inside seal, Simon gasped and struggled to get through the hard rubber. Beside him Wesley shushed every noise, and Simon tried to slow his movements for caution. His heart was thundering in his ears and he could hardly hear Wesley, but he'd begun to remember that they did not want to be heard or caught.

His cutting efforts were completely ineffective. The hard inner rubber only chipped away, and their knife was not long enough to reach through to the outside seal. He couldn't reach the outside to bring in any air.

They used their long screwdriver next. Taking turns they pried it through the strong rubber until they felt the give.

"It's through," Simon gasped. He felt frantic for the air now.

"Stop. Stop," Wesley hissed. "Someone will see."

Simon stopped, trying to catch his breath while he tried to still the panic choking up his throat. "Too bad this thing isn't hollow," he murmured. "We could breathe through it."

"The straws," they both said at once, remembering the juice straws that Rica had thrown into their cart. Simon left Wesley to hold the screwdriver and hurried back to their supplies to find the straws.

It wasn't easy to create enough room beside the screwdriver to insert a straw, but they managed to push one through. Simon watched as Wesley took in the first draw of air from outside. He flinched at the loud sound it made and then hurried to take his own turn.

It wasn't enough. The straw caved in, the air had to be pulled in forcibly, and for the tiring effort of pushing against the screwdriver and pulling in the narrow stream of air, it didn't amount to enough air to make a difference.

Simon groaned. "We have to make some holes," he said. Wesley began shaking his head. The whites of his eyes stood out in the darkness, as trickles of sweat dripped off his eyebrows. "Too noisy," he said. "They'll hear."

"We have to do it," Simon stated.

He made the first hole on the side of the container near their packs. He sat cross-legged on the ceramic tiles and held the drill bit tight against the thick warm metal while he worked the hand tool around and around. It was slow going. Every minute or so he would have to stop and listen intently to the outside sounds.

He had to work quietly with measured deliberate movements. The metal of the container was thick. A cordless drill would have worked more easily, of course. But it would not have been quiet enough, and there would have been no way to recharge batteries anyway.

After more than thirty minutes of steady turning and pausing to listen, Simon slowly pulled the drill backwards to present a thin pencil sized hole in the wall. Simon stared at the pinprick of light. He felt almost as hungry for light as he was for air and he marveled at the wondrous brilliance of the sight for several seconds before he grabbed up a juice straw and brought in oxygen to his starving lungs.

They took turns drilling three more holes, taking their rest time at a drilled hole to breathe air in with a straw.

When their container boasted a hole in each wall Simon leaned back wearily and said, "The air should come in soon now. With a hole on each side like this, it should start flowing in."

The air didn't flow in though. It didn't seem to make any difference at all.

"The holes are too small," Wesley said. He pulled in another breath from his straw and leaned back against the wall. The workmen outside had hours ago completed their work for the day, and once again Simon and Wesley were a little less afraid of whispering back and forth. Temperatures were cooling and the pinpricks of light that they had made in the walls were dimming as twilight fell around them.

Simon sighed and closed his eyes. With his arm he swiped back the sweat on his face and turned the beam of the flashlight toward their tools. "We're going to have to make a bigger hole," he said.

They both decided a bigger hole on one of the walls would be too risky. Sawing through the metal with a hacksaw would be much too noisy, and besides, someone would soon notice a hole on the side of the container. The floor would be their best bet. It was a

167

hard-pressed particleboard, but perhaps easier to cut through than metal.

Nothing was easy about cutting a hole through the floor though. For one thing, the space between the shoulder high skids of ceramic tiles didn't leave enough room for maneuvering. Simon could stand between the ceramic crates and the container wall at the front and at the back but that was all. There was no room to bend over and work.

What they finally worked out was almost comical. Wesley held Simon's feet while Simon hung upside down to work, but there was little that was funny about the effort. Without their efforts and without air they would die soon.

Simon had to first drill two holes through the tough, compressed wood before he could even fit the hacksaw blade in to begin sawing, and then it was incredibly hard to make any progress. The wood turned out to be three or four inches thick and almost as tough to get through as the side-wall of the metal container.

Blood rushed into Simon's head until he thought the pressure would cause his head to explode. Over and over he had to stop and rest gulping down more and more of their precious water while he worked.

The tiny hacksaw blade had no handle and was difficult to hold tightly in sweat slippery fingers. It was not strong enough to turn corners, either. Simon learned that by breaking a blade. He used the hand drill, making holes at each corner so that he could continue cutting in another direction to create the square hole.

It took most of the night to finish. A dim suggestion of light showed through the floor when Simon carefully lifted the little four by four piece of wood out to Wesley.

"Is the air coming?" Wesley asked.

Simon couldn't tell. "Hand me the lighter," he ordered Wesley.

Hope plunged as Simon held the lighter close to his hard — earned square and flicked again and again at the lighter.

168

"It isn't lighting," Wesley whispered needlessly. "Why isn't it lighting?"

Simon couldn't answer. Was the hole too thick to let the air flow inward? Was there something below them that prevented airflow? Desperately he continued to work the mechanism on the lighter feeling the slow prickle of panic fingering through the hairs along his neck.

They wouldn't have time to saw another hole, for it was getting light outside. Soon there would be people and machines around them. They would have to stay quiet.

Then a flame sprouted at the top of the lighter. The small yellow dance of fire shot relief into Simon as intensely as jumping into cool water on a hot day.

"It's coming in," he told Wesley. "The air is coming in now. It just took awhile to find its way in." He closed his eyes and breathed in the air.

"Can you see anything? Can you feel dirt or anything underneath?"

Simon couldn't even fit his fist through the hole. His fingers reached out into cooler air, but there was nothing within reach to touch. Back on top he put the tools down, and then positioned his body to face downward mimicking Wesley who leaned his head toward the hole to breathe in the hint of cooler air.

In his hands, Wesley turned the small piece of wood over and over. "Like a piece of cake," he whispered. "Looks like my mother's pound cake. Small piece though. I might need to ask for a larger portion." There was a smile in Wesley's voice.

Simon was about to tell Wesley that if he wanted a larger portion he would have to start cutting it himself, but Wesley alerted him with a gasp.

"Oh no! This isn't good. They'll see," Wesley hissed. "When they load us, they'll see the underside of the container when the crane picks us up. They'll see the hole!"

Chapter 17

Cutting Through Steel

As welcome as the first whiffs of fresh air felt, fear overshadowed Wesley's relief. A hole in the floor would be sure to bring unwelcomed attention if it was noticed and it would probably be noticed by anyone who looked up if they were lifted from the ground.

"We better put it back," Wesley hissed. He thrust the small square piece of wood towards Simon.

Simon shook his head. "We can't. It will fall right through. There's nothing to keep it from falling through."

"Then one of us will have to hold it there if we feel our container being picked up." Even as he said it, Wesley didn't suppose it would work. It had been hard to hold on and keep their balance while the crane swung them through the air the last time. And even with the container sitting motionless, it had been hard to hold each other steady when they'd been sawing. It would be impossible for Simon to hold the wood in the hole or for him to hold Simon's feet and keep his own balance with the crane jerking them up and around.

Wesley sucked in another breath as he gawked down at the hole they had both slaved to create during the night. It was already growing brighter and he could hear workmen and machinery somewhere in the shipping yard already.

"Something to hold it," he said, whispering to himself. "We need something to hold it in there." His eyes traveled to Simon and then over toward their tools while his brain struggled for options.

The solution, when they'd devised one, felt precarious at best. With the tiny screws from a music cassette tape that Wesley had brought tucked in his packsack, Simon managed to connect the square piece of wood to the metal pieces of the broken hacksaw blade by threading them through the end holes of the blade. The two-sharp sided blades stuck out like arms on either side of the wood, reaching out to keep it from falling through.

"It should hold," Simon whispered.

"Try it," Wesley suggested. He wasn't anxious to close off their air supply any more than Simon was, but he thought they ought to check it out. The screws were tiny, and their shallow reach into the wood seemed fragile. "Be gentle with it!" he admonished Simon.

Moments later Simon turned his head to look up at Wesley. "It's holding," he whispered. Triumphant that the plan had worked, Wesley was straining to see as Simon bent down once more to take the wood back out of the hole when a sudden thump and clang jolted the whole container.

Wesley almost lost his grip on Simon's feet.

"Haul me up. Haul me up!" Simon hissed.

Clunk, clank, clunk clank. From each corner of their box the heavy fall of metal on metal echoed on the roof. They could hear the whirring, whining sounds of the crane now too. Intent on what they had been doing, neither of them had even heard the crane.

"Hang on," Wesley said. His voice came out sharp and loud in his ears startling him after so many days of muffled whispers. But no one could hear them now.

Once again their container was being swung through the air.

When it was dropped down it rang with the sound of steel landing on steel.

"Do you think we're on the floor of a ship?" Simon queried. "Or on top of another container," Wesley suggested. He didn't think they had moved far enough to have been loaded onto a ship, and there were no sounds to indicate that they were on water. "Wouldn't a ship move a bit back and forth with heavy containers dropping down on it?"

"The light," Simon exclaimed. "The light on the back door went out."

Wesley turned his head, squinting towards the holes they'd drilled into the walls of the container. Simon was right. The light shining through the tiny hole on the back wall had gone dark. Something was snug up behind their crate.

Around them the noise was deafening. It sounded as if the crane were dropping containers from a great distance. Metal rang against metal. Machinery screamed. Wesley clutched the cardboard beneath him as their container shuddered again and again. And then, fast as the fall of a heavy black curtain, another hole on another side of them blanked out the light as Wesley turned his face to find Simon in the darkness.

He could barely make out the shine from the whites of Simon's eyes. "I think we've got containers up against the back and the front of ours now," he said out loud.

For another hour or more they listened and waited. Simon took the little cake-sized piece of wood from the bottom of the container, and they lay with their heads close to the edge of the ceramic tile crate to catch the rise of air coming in.

The noise seemed to go on and on. Because it was so incredibly loud, Wesley's head throbbed. He was amazed when he realized that Simon was snoring beside him. Lying on his back, Wesley watched the two pinpricks of light coming in on either side of their container, and then jumped when something landed on top of them.

Beside him Simon stopped breathing for a moment and shifted, and then his even snores began again.

A moment later Wesley flinched as metal rang against metal on his right and another pinprick of light abruptly shut off beside him.

Turning to his other side, Wesley focused his eyes on the tiny circle of light still showing through the right-hand side of the container. It somehow seemed vital to his sanity to be able to keep one light shining. If they all went out it would mean that they were boxed in.

After awhile the noises seemed to be farther away and Wesley realized that he was hungry. He sat up to eat and to take another few swallows of water keeping his gaze fixed on the light coming through in that last remaining hole.

He had stretched out once more on his back with his face towards the light when he noticed something odd. The brightness coming through their last hole was dimming down. Fading. He sat up to stare and blink. A booming thump echoed in the distance somewhere distracting him for a moment, and when he looked back he couldn't see any light through the tiny hole they'd drilled.

Noise continued, but from a distance now sounding muffled and far away.

Wesley closed his eyes and tried to relax. He woke to the smell of food for Simon was eating.

"It's morning," Simon told him before he could ask. "But there's no light coming through any of our holes."

"I know," Wesley said. He sat up slowly, rubbing his sore back. "I think we could be inside a building. A storage place maybe."

Simon stopped chewing. Then he said, "But there's a noise, like a big engine. It's a kind of thrumming sound."

174

"Some kind of generator probably," Wesley said. "There's no movement. If we were on a ship I think we'd feel some movement. Plus, I watched the last light go dark on this side. It didn't slice off so quick like the others but it faded slowly. Like a big door shutting." He used his hand to demonstrate. Then he added, "And I heard a boom like a door had closed."

Wesley could hear Simon begin eating once more. With his mouth half full Simon mumbled, "Well, at least we don't have to worry about going to India then."

"That's right," Wesley remembered. "It's Saturday. The only ship leaving on Saturday was going to India."

The realization gave little relief, however. Being stuck in a huge storage building wasn't a happier fate than being on the way to India. "At least it's not as hot," Wesley said, trying to sound cheerful.

There were still machinery noises and loud clunking sounds of containers being moved around outside, even voices.

None of the noises were happening around them anymore though. It made Wesley's theory about being inside a storage building seem even more likely. Sounds were muffled because there was a wall between them and the outside where work progressed as usual in the shipping yard.

With no voices or movement close around them, they both felt less worried about making noise or turning on their flashlight.

They talked for a while about what their families would be doing at church. Simon wondered aloud if Stefan would find someone else to sing with. Wesley teased Simon about a girl in the Torino church who had always blushed when Simon looked her way, and Simon in turn teased Wesley about the cute Italian girl who had taught a group language class.

Then they reluctantly returned to their immediate dilemma.

"We're running out of water," Wesley said.

Simon let out a long breath. "It's going fast," he said.

The air thickened into silence for a few moments while they both worried. Simon's sigh was audible. "I think we have to get ourselves out of here."

Wesley nodded. It was their only choice now really. With no way of knowing how long their container would be stored, they could be looking at weeks or even months before they were loaded on a ship at this rate. And they would never survive an ocean voyage now with so little water. He sat up, away from the metal wall where he'd been resting. "Hopefully we can find a way out of this building once we get out of the container," he said.

They talked about how they would try to use the cover of darkness to sneak through the shipping yard and the pros and cons of getting in touch with Rica. They had paid to be put in a container going to America. Didn't Rica at least owe them some help?

Wesley grabbed up a few of their small hacksaw blades and followed when Simon went to stand at the back, inspecting the doors. Rica had explained to Simon where to cut their hole so that they would be able to open the doors. They had already drilled a small air hole nearby so Simon quickly went to work on making another hole beside it.

There was room to move the hacksaw blade back and forth in the opening once Wesley had drilled one more hole. The noise almost stopped them from proceeding though because the sawing motion against the hard steel of the container wall seemed dangerously loud after their careful whispering and slow quiet movements.

"No. Stop. It's too loud," Wesley hissed. He felt his face grimacing against the sound.

"I can't help the noise," Simon answered. "We have to get out." He sighed when the small blade snapped in his hands. "These blades aren't strong enough for this job," he said. "And we're running out of them."

Wesley moved his head closer to inspect Simon's progress once he'd handed Simon another hacksaw blade. He could see that

Simon was having difficulty holding on to the blade and generating enough force to bite into the hard metal. The cut he'd made was less than an inch in length and he'd been working steadily for thirty minutes.

When another blade bent in two and Simon began muttering, Wesley took up the long screwdriver and began chipping away at the hard rubber seal between the two doors where they'd stuck their first straw to suck in air from outside. He managed to chink away a bit more of the tough material and, then he poked the end of the screwdriver through and out to the rubber on the outside of the doors. Wesley had been able to gouge away some of the rubber on the inside and on the outside by thrusting the screwdriver back and forth in the opening, but the crack he'd opened was narrow, and it was still too dark to see anything beyond their container.

When his screwdriver hit something hard, Wesley was immediately alarmed because he wasn't sure what had happened. He leaned close to put his eye against the slit he'd opened and then put the screwdriver in once more. He thrust it out twice more. He pulled the screwdriver back in and lay it down quietly on top of the skid of tiles. His head fell heavily against the door. Through the metal he could feel the thrumming noise buzzing through his head. "Stop cutting," Simon said.

Wesley stopped. He wiped the sweat from his face with the arm of his shirt and turned to face Simon. "What?" he asked.

"It's useless." Despair washed through Simon in the ensuing silence, as he said it again more quietly. "It's useless," he whispered. "We won't be able to open the doors."

Wesley didn't ask why not. He stood waiting, panting for air after his exertion.

"There's another container just behind us," Wesley told him. "It's right here. This close," he explained, using his hands to demonstrate. "We could never even push those levers out never mind open the doors or squeeze through. It's right up against us."

For a handful of heartbeats Wesley stood listening to Simon's ragged breaths. The air felt stifling, and they were a container's length away from the little square in the floor bringing air inside. In spite of the heat, Wesley continued chipping away at the hard rubber, as he felt a cold wash of tickly sweat begin to spread up his back and into his face. The sour taste of dread inched up the back of his throat.

Trapped, he thought. Entombed, his mind told him. There was no way out. They would run out of water and then they would die a slow death. With a jerk of his head he snapped off his morbid thoughts; he wasn't ready to give up or die.

"What are we going to do?" Simon asked. His voice sounded thin and controlled, as if he were stopping his own desperate thoughts with great effort. "What do we do?" he repeated.

To answer, Wesley pulled his body back up on top of the crates and sat with his head brushing the roof. What do we do? His mind took up the question and let it duplicate itself into a little song in his head. Was there anything they could do?

He let his head swivel around their tomb as he thought.

"The lights," he said quietly. "They all went off just like that," he snapped his fingers to show Simon who had come to sit beside him. "Remember? They were pinpricks of light and then they were sliced off to dark just like that." Wesley pointed at each of the three walls where the light had gone out so quickly.

"Where they were loading the containers around us, probably," Simon whispered.

Wesley nodded. "Except for the light on this wall." He pointed once more. "On this wall the light faded slowly. Like it might have done if the doors to the storage building were closed." Wesley turned his face towards Simon's. Optimism struggled for some footing as he spoke. "The light didn't slice off quickly on this wall. I don't think there is a container up against us on this side."

For the next few hours Wesley worked with Simon by turns, making a hole in the sidewall of their container where the light had disappeared slowly. To endure the strenuous task, Wesley convinced himself that there would be enough space on the other side for them to squeeze through and escape. However, there was no way to find out for sure.

Wesley sat cross-legged on the top of the skid of ceramic tiles beside Simon and attacked the wall knowing his escape and his very life depended on this work. It was incredibly slow going as the little blades slipped out of his sweaty fingers, others bent over and became useless. Several of Simon's snapped in two. The rippled walls of the container resisted their efforts and made their sawing lines veer crookedly sideways as they worked. The hacksaw blades were running out and little progress had been made.

"It's not working," Simon complained. He paused to sigh and then he reached for the hammer and the chisel.

Wesley shook his head, but didn't voice his worry. It would be noisy, but they would have to take the chance. The first ear shattering, heart stopping crash of sound the hammer made against the chisel into the wall made Wesley hiss, "No! Some one will hear for sure!"

In the darkness he faced Simon, listening. Their own ragged breathing filled the quiet as they waited to see if the bang had alerted anyone. Without another word Simon lifted his hammer and smashed the chisel into the wall once more. Then he stopped to listen again. Three more bangs and another pause to listen.

It was much too loud, Wesley thought. Surely someone would hear and come to investigate. Any moment now, a patrol guard or a night watchman would discover their container. But no one came, and it was taking so long to make any progress. The waiting, the listening time in between each loud bang began to be shorter and shorter, until the BANG, BANG, BANG, went on without any listening time in between.

179

Wesley cringed at the sound and despaired at the tremendous effort it took to make so little headway. A fist-sized hole for reaching an arm through would not be adequate for this plan, and it felt discouraging to watch the cut in the wall growing so slowly knowing that the opening must be big enough to crawl through.

Through the hours of the night and into Sunday morning Wesley took turns hammering at the chisel to tear through the tough metal wall. His ears rang. His fingers and arms cramped up in pain. His hands and his neck stiffened from the strain. When one cut appeared lengthy enough and they decided to change directions, they had to again drill a couple of holes with the hand drill just to allow room for the chisel to work. Cutting across at the bottom of their first cut was even tougher, and cutting upwards proved impossible. Instead they drilled another two holes and worked downward to meet their last cut line.

It looked like a ragged-edged pet door when they were finished. Unlike a pet door that would give and bend when pushed on, this piece of cut wall would not dislodge.

Wesley positioned his feet beside Simon's and struggled to move the metal outwards. "One, two, three push," he commanded. They both pushed. They used all their strength, but nothing budged. They were still trapped!

Chapter 18

Still Trapped

Wesley watched Simon pick up the chisel and hammer one more time. Simon held the chisel against the wall and thwacked it with the hammer as the harsh reverberation sent Wesley's hands to his ears. "Too loud!" Wesley cried.

"We have to get out," Simon shot back at him.

Wesley thought Simon sounded angry or maybe afraid. He cringed as Simon hit the metal again and again with all his strength. The clamor rang through his head and jarred against the steady rhythm of his heart throwing it off kilter. But nothing gave way.

Once more they went back to making more holes and more tedious cuts until finally they were able to inch the cut piece of wall away by bending it outward.

Simon took the first look out.

As Wesley waited while Simon shone the flashlight down and out over stacks of containers and then up at the corners of the storage building, Wesley pushed up on the metal flap to hold the sharp edges away. Cold damp air rushed into the container with an odor of rust, machinery oil and dampness. The noise of the generator sounded louder.

"Can we get out? Did you see a door to the building?" Wesley asked.

Simon turned back to face Wesley. He held the flashlight under his chin and grinned wickedly. "Yes, we can get out," he said. Then he added, "But we're not in a building. We're on a ship."

Wesley's heart thudded over in surprise. "A ship! How do you know? What did you see?"

"The walls slope in. And I saw a hatch in the ceiling, a ship door. There's a real hatch!"

Wesley still wasn't ready to believe.

"I saw it just like that in a movie," Simon insisted. "It's a ship. It is. We're down in the hold. The doors you heard close? They were the doors to this part of the hold I guess, above us."

For a moment Wesley couldn't think of anything to say. The surprise of the news overwhelmed him while worry warred with elation inside him. They were leaving Italy at last. Had they really pulled it off? But where were they going? Were they on their way to India? Could they survive an ocean voyage now? They'd used up most of their water.

"That noise we thought was a generator could be the ship engines."

"I want to see," Wesley said. Suddenly he wanted out of this tin box prison. He needed to look at more than four walls and he needed to breathe again.

Neither proved successful or fulfilling, however. It was just as dark in the hold as it had been inside their container. Although the air felt moist against their skin and they had some movement flowing around them with a coolness they hadn't felt in their container, there was an odd unpleasant smell to it.

Wesley held the flashlight as Simon climbed out of the container and carefully pulled his body over the sharp metal edge so he wouldn't cut himself.

Standing on top of the container next to their own, the jagged hole they had climbed out came to Wesley's chest level. A thrumming sound vibrated into his feet and up his legs. Aiming his flashlight around the vast space surrounding them, Wesley tried to determine their options, but the little flashlight beam didn't carry far. It was extremely difficult to get a big picture of what was around them with so little light. They could see that one container sat on top of theirs, and that other stacks around them stood even taller.

"We're near the top of the pile," Wesley observed. He shivered as he let his light prick downward through the darkness to what he thought must be the ship's floor. What if they'd been loaded first, and placed farther down? Many of the lower containers were boxed in closely on every side with no room to escape.

Positioned towards the middle of the mountain of boxes, their container was among the taller middle stacks. On one side of them, sloping down, two rows of containers were piled only four or five high, and other stacks of metal boxes reached up to the hold's ceiling.

A ship full of containers

183

Above them, just outside their container to the left, Wesley could see a rust rimmed hatch in the ceiling. Aiming his flashlight in that direction he made out a window–like opening in the solid metal that surrounded a high platform. It looked like a viewing area that could be accessed from above deck, a place to inspect the hold. A steep narrow ladder led up to the rusty hatch on an equally rusty bulkhead wall.

In the other direction, on the other side of their container, a sea of darkness loomed. There was no way to see how far it went.

Simon had retrieved the other flashlight and was already moving out to explore. Impulsive as usual, and restless from their four days of confinement, Simon sounded eager, almost excited when he spoke, "Let's go see what's around us," he suggested. "Maybe we can find where there's some light."

"Light! Yes," Wesley agreed quickly. Getting to somewhere, where they could see light sounded worth any amount of effort. His whole body had grown weary of the constant darkness.

Simon had spoken out loud and Wesley didn't bother to hush his words. He felt insulated from the real world down here in the bowels of the ship. Noise and activity still rang out above them, but down here it was empty of life. Only the steady thrum of an engine surrounded them, and Wesley felt safe from listening ears.

They climbed down first. Simon scouted out a place with enough room between the piles of containers to allow movement, and they lowered themselves down hand over hand to the floor, using the tall metal frame pieces caging the containers firmly in their tall stacks. Almost right away they had to crawl up again, and then over top of some lower stacks of containers and down again. In the darkness it was hard to gauge directions, and several times they had to back up or retrace their steps when they came to dead ends or places they could not get through. In such an immense dark chamber it was impossible to see far enough ahead to plan a route. Wesley allowed his flashlight to point out safe steps for his feet as he followed the jiggling beam of Simon's flashlight ahead of him.

His head jerked up when Simon's excited voice yelled back to him.

"There are words on some of these containers," Simon called back.

Wesley shone his flashlight over the containers around him. Sure enough, several had painted letters on the sides of them. The ones he could see up close had letters that made no sense to him.

"H–y–un–dai," Simon sounded out." Hyundai. That's a country, right?"

Wesley frowned. "Hyundy is a truck company, isn't it? Or cars? Maybe Hyundai is an American spelling." He stood with Simon, mouthing out the sound of the letters.

"I think it's a country," Simon repeated.

"I think you were probably playing soccer when you were supposed to be in geography class," Wesley teased.

He moved to the side of one container and shone his narrow beam of light along another bottom row of containers. His hopes jumped as he read out the tall, white lettering written on three containers. "CANADA," he shouted back at Simon. The loudness of his voice sounded frightening. Lowering it, he repeated, "All these containers here say Canada. We're going to Canada!" He heard the excitement in his voice and that startled him almost as much as his shout.

Had he been feeling so discouraged that a flicker of hope could feel astonishing?

Simon sounded upbeat and full of life also. "So maybe we could be going to India on the way to Canada?"

Wesley snorted. "India is not on the way to Canada," he said. "It's the other direction."

In front of him a few paces, Wesley heard Simon chuckle. "Yeah, well, what can I say? I probably was playing soccer during geography lessons."

The darkness was too thick and the containers were too tightly packed to allow them to learn much about their surroundings at first, but after a time of moving steadily away from their container Simon pointed to an area, in the distance, on one side of the ceiling that looked brighter.

"There must be a light over there," Simon spoke.

They still needed their flashlights for every step, in spite of that distant light; that gave them a better sense of direction and a new hope.

Wesley felt surprised when they came up to the end of rows of containers to stand up against a wall. Smooth white painted steel barricaded them from moving towards where the light shone. When they noticed a ladder on the bulkhead that reached as high as the container stacks and divided their container section from the next section, Wesley followed Simon eagerly to a half moon shaped opening in the wall. On top of the wall they could finally see where the light was coming from. It was a simple bulb light looped about with a metal cage and shining near another hatch in the ceiling. A wide sloping stairway led to this hatch, but the whole area appeared to be impossible to reach.

Even though containers were stacked high to the ceiling and tight up to the wall on their side of the bulkhead, there was a black depth of nothingness on the other side between them and the lighted hatch. The deep chasm yawned like an open pit ready to swallow them. From where Wesley and Simon were perched on the top of the wall it looked to be a very long way down to the bottom. Long, rather narrow beams stretched over to the starboard wall of the ship.

"If we go along this beam to the side it looks like we could climb down over there," Simon suggested. "It's a steel beam," he persuaded. "Basically a reinforcement strut. It's strong enough."

Wesley stood uncertain, watching Simon step carefully out onto the beam and then step back again. He stifled a shiver, and found himself holding his breath.

Simon finally opted to shimmy across sitting down, and Wesley followed in the same manner. He draped one leg over each side and pulled himself forward inch-by-inch.

Over half an hour had passed before they reached the sloping starboard wall of the ship.

From there it wasn't difficult to climb down to the ship's floor. Evenly spaced steel shelf–like reinforcements on the wall acted like a sort of stairway.

A mire of greenish, rusty water and slippery goo greeted them on the ship's floor. They stepped carefully, avoiding the puddles of liquid while using their flashlights to find safe footing. The air felt several degrees colder down here and the sharp, damp odor almost hurt Wesley's nostrils.

When the ship's horn blasted, Wesley dropped to a crouch.

Simon looked back at him, eyes wide.

"Another ship going by?" Wesley asked.

Simon shrugged. "Or just leaving port waters and moving out of the bay into open water?"

For a while longer Wesley followed Simon, exploring the dark cavern of the ship's hold near what they both decided now must be close to the bow of the ship. He swept his flashlight in a slow arc from left to right trying to see what was around them. A labyrinth of giant pipes cluttered an area along the starboard wall near where they had climbed down. Dust and grime clung to everything. But the lighted hatch and the stairs leading to it gave the impression of regular use. It also appeared to be the only doorway to escape from the ship's hold in this section. Unlike the shelves they'd climbed down, the door, the steps up and the railing were free of the thick dust coating everything else. Paint had even been worn away on the wider metal stairs. Crewmen obviously used this area to come and go.

The metal cage-encased light bulb showed them their footing as they moved in for a closer look. They switched off their flashlights to conserve the batteries, but they dared not linger in the area long. There were no good hiding spots and at any moment the hatch could be opened. Would there be enough time to crouch into a darker spot and avoid detection once someone started opening the hatch?

Nervous about such possibilities, they both crept back to the starboard wall and began moving out of the light's reach. Wesley froze to stillness when Simon shot out a hand to cut through the air, indicating that he should stop. Straining his ears he listened for whatever had alerted Simon. Sounds above deck were still there, but there was another noise now, an odd sound.

Wesley listened. "Water," he whispered, finally. Simon was too far ahead to hear him, so he spoke aloud. "I can hear water sloshing against the side here."

Wesley realized that the vibration beneath his feet had changed as well. The buzzing sensation was higher pitched as if the ship were moving faster. "We better get back to the container," he said. "If we've moved out onto open sea the ship will probably get rocking more. It might be hard to move around in here."

The ship never did seem to get rocking though. The only movement Wesley could detect was a gentle rolling type of motion.

Back in their container they drank more of their dwindling water supply, ate some of their spongy bread and then lay dozing away the hours. Wesley slept and woke, and slept again with no sense of whether it was day or night in the constant dark. He could not even tell if the ship was moving sometimes, because the movement was so subtle.

After what Wesley calculated was their second day at sea, they both began to relax. Wesley found the lemons at the bottom of their food bag that Rica had recommended they bring along to settle their stomachs if they got seasick. He held them up to show Simon. "Maybe we won't need these," he said.

"Yeah, this is great," Simon agreed. "This is nothing. I can live with this. But, of course, it could still get rough."

It didn't get rough though for the ship stopped.

Noise began above them, and the sounds of machines could be heard. Banging and booming began once more. The whine of the gantry cranes began again, along with the resounding bangs of more containers either being loaded or unloaded. Were they in another port?

Worry came flooding back. There were plenty of spaces around them. The hold doors could open at any moment to add more containers. Or perhaps they were in port to unload a few containers? They might even unload their container! The jagged hole they had sawed in their container would be noticed if either happened.

Hiding seemed like their only option.

Panic fueled them as they clamored out of their container and climbed down and up and over. Fear of being seen won out over caution. Wesley slipped and almost fell in his haste to scramble down the metal struts along the corner of the container stacks. Simon misjudged a footing, dropped his flashlight, and then had to retrace his steps to retrieve it.

Once again Wesley shimmied across the long beam, following Simon's fluttering flashlight beam. They went directly to the maze of pipes this time for it was the best place they could think of to hide in as the whole area was covered in dirt.

Their careful footsteps stirred up clouds of choking dust, their fingers sank deeply into the foul silt—like stuff wherever they reached out for a hold, and the grime quickly coated their clothing as they maneuvered into a place to hide.

The pipes were enormous things, large enough to provide cover for them if anyone peered down from the hold doors or came down the ladder, but they were high up on the ship's walls. They could stay hidden quite easily in several spots, but they would have to hang on to keep from tumbling out of their perch. The spots where they could wedge their bodies into sitting positions to remain concealed were anything but relaxing.

Wesley strained his ears to hear the sounds coming through the ship's wall. They were close to the ceiling of the hold where they hid. Along with machines and crashing and banging noises, Wesley could also hear voices. Workers were somewhere close, shouting back and forth to each other. Although the sound was muffled, Wesley could not detect any words or even which language was being used.

He snuggled his knees in tight for a better hold. He felt relieved to have found a spot so well concealed, but he had barely settled in to catch his breath before a terrible realization occurred to him. He groaned aloud and created another smudge on his forehead as his hand came up to thump his head. "We should have brought the water," he said. "And some food."

Simon didn't immediately understand Wesley's anguish, so Wesley explained. "If they load more containers we probably won't be able to get back inside to get our stuff. They could put a container right up against the hole we cut. They could even take up our container. Put it onshore. Wherever that is!"

Simon breathed out a long sigh. "We have to go back," he said.

Every clunk and boom above them jarred their muscles into nervous twitches on their next hurried journey to their container and back. Crossing the beam, Wesley hurried as fast as he could convince his legs to move. He didn't know if he was more afraid that the hold doors would open and catch him and Simon only half way across, or more fearful that one of them would slip in their haste, and plunge to the rusty metal floor. By the time they returned to their hiding spot with some essentials, Wesley's limbs were shaking with stress and exhaustion.

It was terribly uncomfortable wedged in between the pipes, and it wasn't safe enough to relax. They both had to hold tight just to keep from falling.

It was a long drop to the bottom.

Chapter 19

Surviving Through the Storm

Simon shifted in his precarious roost. He was so exhausted that he could not force himself to stay awake and he kept relaxing his grip as weariness claimed him. Several times his head banged against a dusty pipe, waking him. He would open his eyes at every loud boom, grab for a better hold when he felt his body slide, and then, a few seconds later, he would feel his head fall forward jerking him awake with a movement or the feel of his head hitting metal.

Wesley wasn't fairing any better. "It's too dirty and too uncomfortable to sleep here," he said. "We'd probably fall if we dropped off to sleep."

Simon didn't argue or admit that he'd been falling asleep in spite of the dirt and the uncomfortable spot. He listened, chuckling at times as Wesley told him about some of the horrible places he had slept while in Italy.

"This one abandoned house had mattresses on the floors," Wesley said. "It was dark and I just crashed out, tired, you know? I even pulled some old blankets over myself." Wesley paused to make a noise of disgust. "In the morning, as soon as there was some light and I could see the filth on the bed and on the blankets, I felt so sick." Wesley shook his head. "It was so gross. It turned my stomach," he finished.

Simon murmured his own disgust, imagining the scene. But the filth around him seemed almost as repulsive. Was it safe to go back to their container yet?

Cocking his head to listen, Simon said, "I think I hear water movement again. We must have left the dock." He paused, trying to read Wesley's expression in the darkness. "If we're back at sea, maybe we should go back to the container."

As anxious as he had been to leave their box, Simon had begun to remember how much cleaner it had been lying on ceramic tiles. Stretching out his legs with something to lie down on would be welcome too. They still had one bottle of water left; it wasn't time to go above deck yet.

The ship began really rocking by the time Simon and Wesley had made it across the beam to their bulkhead full of containers. A steady, rolling motion kept them off balance as they worked their way back through the containers. In this section the noise became much louder as containers banged each time the ship rolled clanging against their upright metal struts.

"Careful of your fingers," Simon yelled back to Wesley as he climbed. With the containers shifting as the ship rocked, climbing up the metal struts became dangerous. Simon tried to time the placing of each of his hands as he pulled himself upwards. "Climb, climb, climb. Stop and take your fingers out of danger. Climb again. Watch carefully!" The containers were shifting back and forth fairly regularly, but every once in awhile they would lurch without warning. Simon knew first hand about the agony involved with a smashed finger.

Less than a year ago an accident had crushed his thumb while working on a construction job. As an illegal immigrant medical help had not been an option, even when his thumb became badly infected Simon had to suffer for days. Vividly he remembered how the pain had throbbed on and on, keeping time with his pulse as his finger turned blacker and more swollen.

Pulling themselves up close to the back of their container, Wesley pointed out the new seals that were on the back of their box. "That must be what they were doing when we heard the noises at the door," he said. "Maybe they say where we are going."

Simon couldn't get close enough or get a good look though; he wasn't even sure he wanted to know. He guessed that it would cheer them both to find out they were on their way to Canada, but what would be the point of discovering that India or Asia or Australia was their destination? It wasn't like they could do anything about their fate at this point for they no longer had any choice of destination.

Inside the container at last Simon settled down to eat. He told Wesley about his painful smashed thumb and then began talking about some of the harrowing escapes he'd managed while working at his construction job in Italy. "They were always coming around to check papers," Simon exclaimed. "My boss would make this quick motion when he saw them coming. He'd throw out his hand at me like so." Simon made the cutting movement with his own hand remembering as he made it that Wesley probably couldn't see the gesture in the blackness. "That's all he would do," Simon continued. "Just that quick movement that meant; take off get out of here fast. One time when an inspector came I thought I was caught for sure. I had to jump down from the second floor of this place we were building."

"At least you had a job."

Simon stared into the darkness in the direction of Wesley's voice. "It was harder for you, coming to Italy later. There were more immigrants looking for work so I kept asking around, trying to get some work for you."

"I know. I know you tried. If I could have just spoken the language better."

Simon nodded. "That was the problem. If you had known Italian better you probably could have found something."

They argued good naturedly about what day it was after that. Wesley felt certain that it was Monday afternoon. Simon calculated that it must be Tuesday just before dawn.

When conversation stalled, Simon sat listening to the ship as it spoke between their words. It was a language as alien to him as the sound of foreigners speaking. Half the sounds he heard made no sense to him.

Gradually the noise around them grew louder. As the ship moved faster, the containers began to clank with an echoing din with other noises beginning above them. An occasional loud crash and sometimes the sound of something heavy scraping along in a slide across the deck got them both talking again, guessing about what might be happening above their hold. They had to raise their voices to be heard.

Simon lay down on his back looking up at the dark roof of the container. The motion of the ship nudged his head this way and that way jostling his brains and stirring his thoughts. He knew that very soon he and Wesley would have to climb up the ladder by the light and open the hatch door to go above deck. They could not last much longer without water. It was risky. The stories of stowaways being thrown overboard were common knowledge. If they weren't thrown overboard when they were discovered, they would most likely be locked up somewhere perhaps separately, or in a prison worse than this container. Simon had heard that ship captains were notoriously unforgiving about intruders boarding their ship illegally. A ship's captain could be held accountable by customs officials, sometimes forced to feed and house asylum seekers for long periods of time when immigration officials disallowed entry.

Although going up above deck was a danger they would have to face, they would soon die of thirst if they stayed below.

When Simon began to drift towards sleep once more, he fashioned a daydream that he and Wesley could sneak topside, find water, and then hide somewhere before anyone saw them. It could work out, he thought.

In the constant darkness Simon fell in and out of sleep, never feeling sure if he'd been asleep for hours or minutes unless he checked his watch. Even then he wasn't sure; was it 3 in the morning or 3 in the afternoon?

Shock froze him to stillness when he lifted the water to his lips. They were on their last bottle of water, and the line of liquid fell just below the paper label now. He could hardly believe the water had disappeared so fast. They had been only wetting their lips and mouths since starting this last bottle of water, but it still had fallen too quickly. Strong determination was needed to tip up the bottle of water and only wet his mouth with it when he desperately wanted to swallow mouthfuls of the sweet liquid and quench his thirst.

Craving water kept Simon from wanting to eat anything now. He wasn't that hungry anyway, and as soon as he ate anything his thirst would became more intense. It was easier not to bother with food.

Later, when he woke to find himself rolling into the wall of the container, Simon had no idea of the day or the time. Wesley had crashed up against his back and the ship's rocking had grown more violent. All around them containers had taken on a more urgent banging as they heaved and struggled and slammed in their iron bars. Simon could hear their own box clanking into its metal struts, a ringing noise that went on and on faster than before.

Simon watched Wesley groan his way into wakefulness and struggle to sit up, sounding as though he was in pain. Simon peered at him anxiously. "Are you okay?" he asked. When Wesley didn't answer Simon switched on his flashlight to look at his friend. A clutch of worry hit him hard at the sight of Wesley's pale sweaty skin and distraught expression. Wesley obviously was not okay for he looked very ill.

Hurriedly Simon grabbed at the food bag and groped for the lemons. "Try a lemon," he offered. "It might help the sea sickness."

Wesley reached weakly for the sour fruit and then bit into it like an apple. After a moment, Simon did the same.

As the ship fell into a sickening rhythm of falling and rising, Simon lay down on his stomach with his chin on the cardboard. To keep himself from rolling around he spread his arms out wide. When he closed his eyes it felt as if he were flying. The whole container moved with him; his own private airplane.

The hours passed slowly. Simon tried to convince himself that the rocking had changed or that the pitching of the ship had started to lessen. He knew it wasn't true. If anything, the ship had begun to pitch more frequently and plunge more deeply. It was a storm, Simon decided, not just the chop of open sea. If it was a storm, it would pass, it couldn't last much longer. Could it?

"Hang on," he yelled to Wesley once more as the ship climbed up, tipping them almost upright. Then "Here we go," he would yell out as the vessel plunged.

Even lying down, Simon struggled to gain a sense of balance. He wasted energy gripping tightly to keep his body from being flung upwards only to have to change his pose to keep from sliding sideways. It was hard to tell which direction the ship would lurch next. Swells became irregular and the deep rolls were interspersed now with jerks and staggers as the ship hesitated and then heeled, slewing in one direction and then abruptly, violently, into another.

It was a nightmare he couldn't awaken from; a crazy ride he couldn't stop. When he managed to check the time he guessed the worst part of the storm had been tossing their ship for only five hours, but it felt like five days. He'd been struggling to hold on and keep from being thrown around the container for so long that his entire body ached with the strain. His empty stomach lurched and roiled in discomfort, and it felt as if there were loose material inside his head being sloshed back to front and side-to-side within his skull.

At the sound of Wesley making retching noises, the bile in Simon's stomach rose high into his throat in a wave of sympathy. Was he going to be sick? Should he make his way to the rear of the container with Wesley in case he was going to throw up?

Twelve hours into the gale, Simon feared more than his own seasickness. The ship was in trouble. It sounded as if parts of the vessel had torn loose, as if a fifty-ton truck had come unleashed on the deck and was now acting like a battering ram topside.

An assortment of things seemed to be loose, shooting across the deck to smash against other things with alarming explosions. Possibly every container above deck had been loosed from their metal cages. Containers that hadn't toppled into the angry sea by now must be unfastened up there on the deck, Simon thought. He could no longer detect the hum of the engines or sense any direction to the ship's floundering and bucking. Had the ship developed a list to one side? It felt that way. Perhaps it was even taking on water. Perhaps the crew was getting ready to launch the lifeboats. Or had they abandoned ship already? If so, he and Wesley would sink with the doomed vessel and no one would know they were in here. No one would even know of their watery fate.

Through the storm

The stories that Marc entertained them with, stories that Simon had smiled away as exaggerations, felt horribly realistic now. Marc's tales of ships colliding in a storm, throwing containers in high seas, slicing into coastal rocks in a gale now, they were believable. With the ship pitching so brutally, Simon had no trouble supposing that heavily secured containers could come unlashed. And he wondered if the cargo had shifted in seas this rough? Even a ship the size of five football fields could simply roll over and disappear to the depths of the ocean if it became unbalanced.

As he listened to the vessel groan and scream, Simon thought he heard the sounds of metal buckling and steel girders snapping. Was it breaking apart? In their brief exploration Simon had not been able to tell if they were aboard a giant international container ship or an older, smaller vessel made for hugging the coast for they could not see beyond the other bulkhead. They had seen a lot of rust though, with places that appeared to have been patched up with epoxy putty. Perhaps the ship was ancient, trying to make one more run for profit. A fierce squall like this one could take such a vessel to the ocean floor.

Every drop had been drained from the water bottle by this time with nothing left to even wet his tongue. When Wesley began eating another lemon to settle his tormented stomach, Simon joined him. Vomiting felt like a small concern along side his other worries, but misery directed his actions now. And the lemon offered a refreshing wetness in his mouth.

Several times Simon opened his mouth to say something to Wesley and then stopped. The noise had become so deafening that conversation would have been difficult, and Wesley sounded more miserable than Simon felt. He was staying near the front of their container instead of crawling to the back to be sick. Simon figured he had nothing left in his stomach to throw up any longer, but he still continued to retch into a plastic bag.

Simon felt a wave of compassion flood him as he watched his best friend gag and heave again and again while struggling to keep from being thrown about the container. It would be cruel to burden Wesley with his terrible thoughts. He didn't want to give words to the fears torturing him anyway so he kept his words going heavenward instead.

He was into his "top of the line" prayers by this time. With all the sincerity of a heart that knows it may not be able to beat much longer, Simon pleaded with God to save them. He reminded God that he had some very noble plans for his life that would be a blessing to his Lord. He told God that he had chosen this road in order to serve Him. He was paying this price for freedom to gain the privilege of being able to worship Him.

As the storm continued Simon claimed every promise in the Bible that he could remember. He pledged his life away in degrees, bargaining with everything he could think to offer. Imploring God to look down and have mercy, he swore obedience in all areas of his life. He vowed he would be a better person. He would live to help others. He would be a credit to his Creator throughout the rest of his life if God would only intervene and spare his life.

After some time Simon noticed a tune running in his head. When he focused on the familiar melody, the words came back to him effortlessly, comforting him.

"In the dark of the midnight how I oft hid my face,
When the storm howled above me
And there was no hiding place.
Mid the crash of the thunder
Precious Lord hear my cry.
Keep me safe till the storm passes by.

'Till the storm passes over,
'Till the thunder sounds no more,
'Till the clouds roll forever from the sky.
Hold me fast, let me stand
In the hollow of Thy hand.
Keep me safe 'till the storm passes by."

By Mosie Lister

Chapter 20

No More Water, Too Sick to Care

Wesley had never been more frightened or more ill in his entire life.

His stomach felt emptied of its contents and its strength. Nothing was left to throw up anymore, but he continued to heave.

The lemons he'd eaten had helped his queasy innards for awhile, but the sour fruit was long gone. He was thirsty and exhausted and almost too miserable to feel afraid, almost too sick to realize that his survival appeared less and less likely.

The ship was breaking apart. He hadn't spoken his fears aloud to Simon, but nothing else could explain the terrible noises he'd been hearing. The stories that Marc had told them of older, rusted ships breaking into pieces during storms repeated in his head frightening him anew with each squeal, crash and groan.

Once, according to Marc, a thousand pound piece of steel pipe broke its lashings during a storm while crossing the Atlantic.

The deck of the ship was all but destroyed before the crew managed to control it with lines.

Perhaps something like that was happening above board on their ship right now? Maybe the horrendous crashing noises were normal? Or could it be that every noise was simply heightened, echoing louder than normal because they were below deck?

In an attempt to lighten his anxiety, Wesley told himself that container ships plowed through storms on a regular basis. Thousands of merchant ships crisscrossed these waters and only a few ever went down. They were built for rough weather like this.

But his fears had begun to override all such reassurances. At some point he knew that deep-sea vessels and huge diesel engines were no match for high seas and strong winds. Marc had spoken of ninety mile an hour winds and forty-foot high crests. One gale he spoke of had been so fierce that direction had been sacrificed for survival. As Marc told it, the quartermaster had lashed himself to a bulkhead in order to continue steering the ship. In that storm the brave seaman had tacked back and forth, speeding up in the trough to maintain control, slowing just before the crest so he wouldn't pound his ship apart. Was someone just as proficient at the helm now? It didn't feel as if anyone had control of the ship or the direction.

Was God still watching? "Stay at the helm, God. Please," Wesley groaned.

He'd stopped crawling to the back in order to throw up. He hadn't the strength to move that far in the lurching container. It took too long, trying to crawl during the upswings, and then pausing to take a firmer grip during the crashes. His retching was producing nothing but dry heaves now anyway. With waning energy he held tight as the ship climbed steeply up, up, and then slammed down, and down and down, as if it could not find a bottom. When the vessel dropped off the top of the swell it felt as though he was being flung off a tall building or that the elevator had dropped ten stories. He knew that if he let go he could be flung onto his feet or land on his head.

The rolling swells had long since ceased being regular. An erratic variation of jolts and slams and sideways pitches kept him continually off balance and unsure of which way his body would be flung next. The noise around him was overpowering.

When he could organize his thoughts to make sense, he prayed. "God, you are still my hope," he cried. But he wasn't sure he remembered what hope felt like. "Dear Father in heaven, I want to serve you. I want to sing for your glory. I have given you my heart, my trust. You have the power to calm this storm. Please God. Please stop this storm!"

In the constant noise and tumult of motion it felt hard to concentrate, even on words of prayer. Wesley's thoughts turned and tumbled with the tempest. He tried to think of the story of Jesus and his disciples out on the lake of Galilee. There had been a terrific storm then, too. Jesus had stilled it with His words. The Bible story jumped in and out of his memory though and he couldn't remember any details. Snatches of thoughts, half-formed ideas, conversations with Simon, flashes of images of his home and his family all vied for control of his brain in turn. Wesley wondered if perhaps this was what people meant when they said that their entire life flashed before them, when they thought it was the end and they were dying. Was this the end? It was a question suddenly too heavy for his mind to hold up for consideration.

His tongue felt stuck to the roof of his dry mouth. Sweat had plastered his hair against his forehead, but he felt cold and shivery. Time had ceased to have any meaning; it had always been dark. Rough rolling movements had existed forever in this world. This crashing, shrieking, clunking noise was part of the only reality he knew.

What had life been like before?

He couldn't remember.

Several eternities later he attempted to lift his head. It had grown enormously heavy. With one hand Wesley reached out a feeble hand to feel for Simon's arm beside him. He had no words, but with his touch he told Simon everything he needed to say. Through shaky fingers, barely touching Simon's sleeve, Wesley confided to Simon all that was in his heart. He knew Simon understood, and he knew that Simon believed. Simon's prayers were no doubt joining Wesley's own pleas for help at this very moment.

He didn't think there was enough moisture left in his body to allow for tears, but he felt his eyes sting anyway as his emotions squeezed in tight. A flood of unfathomable gratitude filled him for having a friend like Simon. Having Simon nearby provided a comfort he could scarcely comprehend for he knew this misery would be unbearable alone.

Wesley blinked to clear his vision, and then blinked again. Something seemed to have changed; there was a new sound, or perhaps only the absence of an old sound. Had the ship stopped moving so violently? Had they passed through the worst of the storm?

It was another few hours before Wesley let himself believe that the ship was going to stay afloat. He lay prone on his hard bed of ceramic tiles with a desperate thirst, a throbbing headache, and a weakness that had invaded every muscle. His stomach no longer rebelled or tried to push up into his throat. Perhaps the ocean had grown calmer, or perhaps he had grown used to the motion of the sea. Maybe his stomach muscles were merely too tired to respond to seasickness anymore.

Days crawled by.

From time to time Wesley heard Simon say something, but the words swept by him like a racing tide. The meaning presented itself for a second or two and then fell out of reach, like waves snatching away a glimpse of treasure on the sand in a moving tide.

His mouth felt full of sand and there was barely moisture enough to lick his dry lips. Was he even capable of speaking? His tongue might not be able to form words to answer Simon anyway, even if he could work out how to respond.

The din of banging and clanking rang in his head. The sound went on and on, and on, an incessant torment, tiring him more severely than any physical work or exercise had ever done threatening his very sanity. He couldn't sleep. He dreamed instead, existing in a gauzy world of nightmares. Tattered wisps of dream images floated though his mind, too far out of reach to pull into awareness. When discomforts jolted him into a different level of consciousness, Wesley felt uneasy about something he could not recall.

"Wesley! Wesley, wake up." It was Simon's voice. Simon was shaking him. The words came into Wesley's head like the muffled tones of a bell. He felt as though he had been hearing the same words from Simon for some time. He struggled to bring them into focus. "I'm awake," Wesley tried to say. No words came out on his first try though. His tongue moved painfully in his mouth, dry and sluggish like something that didn't belong in there. Opening his mouth for another try at sound, Wesley felt a painful peeling sensation deep in his mouth as if parts of his throat had been stuck together.

The ship was still rocking, and the containers were still banging around them, but it felt almost civilized after the wild turmoil of the storm. Wesley struggled into a sitting position, trying to unfog his brain and listen to what Simon was saying. The word "overboard" seized his attention.

"Thrown overboard?" Wesley squeaked.

Simon stopped speaking and then started again. "I'm saying that even if we get thrown overboard, at least we'll see the sun again."

Wesley nodded. Seeing the sun sounded like a prize worth drowning for. His body longed for daylight.

"We can't stay here," Simon repeated. "We have to take the chance. We have to go above deck and ask for water."

"Okay," Wesley managed. "Water. Okay. Let's go. I can make it."

The journey to the ladder took twice as long this time. They carried their packs with their clothes and the last of their food on their backs, and the small extra weight pulled Wesley's body down. He was so much weaker this time that his limbs moved sluggishly.

They didn't seem to respond as readily climbing down the wall of containers, or along the beam. He'd never felt so tired and several times he looked down at his legs or his hands, wondering why they had ceased working as dependably.

Wesley let Simon lead the way up the sloped stairway to the hatch. He watched in silence as Simon pushed at the hatch, searched for any kind of handle, pushed again and then started banging.

In spite of his agreement to come out of hiding, it took all his will power not to yell for Simon to stop. The banging sounded loud, and though he longed for the hatch to open, he dreaded it, too. After hiding so long in shadow and taking such extreme efforts to avoid detection, the racket of Simon's banging jolted him like the sound of an obscenity.

Wesley's watch had stopped at eleven o'clock. Simon's read four thirty. By Simon's calculations it was afternoon, but Wesley didn't think Simon knew for sure. No matter the time, however, someone was bound to be on watch and hear the banging. Wouldn't they?

When Simon grew weary of banging and pushing against the hatch, Wesley took his turn. Then they both struggled together to push against the white painted steel door.

It wouldn't budge.

They stopped to rest, sitting tight against each other on the hard metal stairs in the guise of telling each other they should stop to listen. In reality, their strength was ebbing. Wesley was barely able to hold to the railing of the ladder with one hand and reach out to pound the hatch with his other.

"If only we had our tools . . ." Simon ventured.

Wesley heard himself groan. All the way back to the container? Then carry tools all the way back here again? He wasn't sure he had the strength.

His desperate need for a drink of water fueled him this time, but neither of them could move very quickly. Wesley stood, panting to catch his breath on the roof of the container beside their own container and grabbed the chisel and then the hammer and the other tools that Simon handed out to him. Once again, he followed as Simon led them back to the hatch where they'd left their packs.

The noise of the hammer blows on the hatch rang shrill and almost painfully against their eardrums. Simon managed a dozen blows to the metal before he stopped to rest. Wesley tried to listen for footsteps or the sound of a turning handle on the hatch but his ears were still ringing.

They tried the hammer and the chisel when the strident sounds of their hammering brought no results. Simon figured he might be able to pry the tip of the chisel into the crack along the hatch and force something to give, or open.

Neither of them was very surprised when the plan failed.

Wesley felt dizzy by now. Twice he caught himself looking down, wondering if he would feel the impact of landing if he suddenly fainted.

When Simon decided to attempt breaching the door by pounding the chisel into the metal with the hammer, he needed both his hands for the job. Wesley had to hold Simon steady to keep his friend from falling backwards when he took a swing at the chisel. Stars spun in the darkness behind Wesley's eyelids as his eyes involuntarily squeezed shut with each piercing crash of metal smacking metal.

It was a wonder that Simon had enough energy left in his body for the task, Wesley thought. The force of his efforts reverberated like a jackhammer on slow speed. But Simon couldn't continue such blows very long.

After a few more attempts Simon's shoulders slumped with failure. "Not even a dent," he complained. "The metal is so hard I can't even make a dent!"

"We should try yelling," Wesley suggested.

"If they didn't hear this . . ." Simon threw up a hand to explain the futileness of such things.

"But it's a different sound," Wesley insisted. "With the ship rocking all the time maybe the guys up there get used to banging sounds and clanging metal-on-metal. Maybe they would hear voices."

Simon shrugged his acceptance of Wesley's words. The wire encased light bulb on the port wall shone against the hatch and the side of Simon's face at this angle, and Wesley paused a breath to stare at his friend. Simon's eyes were red rimmed. They looked somehow unfamiliar. Grime smudged his cheek. His long hair stuck out on the back of his head and the dark beard on Simon's face gave evidence of their lengthy confinement.

Wesley had a sudden, odd sense that he had been cast in some sort of horror movie without his consent. Nothing felt real. Even their voices, when they began to holler and shout as loud as they could, sounded creepy and alien.

Yelling sapped their energy more savagely than hammering. Even though they waited, resting their sore throats after each screaming session, no one came to open the hatch.

"Should we try the other hatch?" Wesley asked.

They both knew their chances were slim at the other hatch. Even from a distance, as they'd played the light of their flash lights over that hatch, they had been able to see the thick grime and the rust on the narrow ladder leading up to the rusty hatch. There had been no light by that hatch. No sign of use. If this larger, well-used hatch wouldn't open for them, the other was even less likely to move.

Getting back over there felt daunting, too. Wesley felt as weak as an infant as tired as an old, old man.

He nodded in agreement though when Simon said, "Let's do it." Somehow, someway, they had to escape this dark tomb or make someone hear them. Soon it would be too late. Very soon now, he would not have any more energy to try.

"A song we sing. A song like no other." The words played over in his mind, comforting him. . . . "the struggles He went through gives us the hope to press on" . . .

Chapter 21

Am I Ready to Meet My God?

The song Wesley hummed so continuously now lent calm to Simon. He knew that their time was short, but having the words of that familiar song go through his head encouraged him somehow. The words were truth to him and the story of God's love *was* "a song like no other". The price of freedom that God had paid was far and above anything Simon was enduring.

Simon's strength was almost spent. His body was changing, weakening. He'd been pushing back the prickles of panic that kept threatening to steal his control, but its terrifying tentacles kept growing back, a hardy weed that wouldn't die.

They had been no more successful at the rusty hatch than they had been at the one with the light. They were trapped in this hold. They'd managed to saw their way out of their container, but now they were trapped inside another larger box; a box just as dark and frightening. One they couldn't cut their way out of. There appeared to be no escape.

The slump of Wesley's shoulders prevented Simon from talking about the futility of their situation. He reached out a hand when Wesley staggered and even tried to make a joke about practicing steps for a slow dance. Neither of them laughed.

They were sitting on top of a container near the rusted hatch now. They had stopped to "just rest a minute", as Simon had suggested. But Simon didn't know what they were going to do after their "rest", or where they were going next. Wesley appeared to be even weaker than he was. Being so sick during the storm had taken a terrible toll and Simon wasn't sure if Wesley could make it back across the beam to the other hatch.

A surge of compassion for his friend felt like a boulder in his chest. He closed his eyes as he tried to draw breath around it. His head ached with words he couldn't find. He knew Wesley did not blame him for this suffering, but he felt responsible, unexpectedly full of regret. Had he talked Wesley into this idea? Was it his fault that they were here now, so close to death? Having his best friend here with him felt like a gift he didn't deserve, a gift he would willingly give up if he could save Wesley from this fate.

Simon reached into his pack for the bread. "We should keep up our strength," he said. It would make them even thirstier, but it might provide some necessary energy. "Just a few bites," he coaxed.

"No." Wesley turned away and put out his hand against the offer.

"Pretend it's a slice of cold mamaliga," Simon tried.

But Wesley only shook his head.

Simon took two bites before he gave up trying to eat. "You're right, it's awful," he said to Wesley. "Even worse than cheese, right?". He knew how much Wesley hated any kind of cheese. But Wesley was strangely quiet. The hang of his head spelled despair. The dust coating his hair made it appear grey as if he had aged into an old man in the last few days.

Abruptly Simon stood. "Let's go back to the other hatch," he said.

Wesley groaned. "Why?"

Because I'm not ready to curl up and die, Simon wanted to say. Because, I want us to live, he thought. But the words caught in his throat as he watched Wesley laboriously get to his feet. Attempting an encouraging lift to his voice he said, "Because there is more of a chance that the crew use that hatch and that someone might be passing by and hear us."

They would not give up, he decided. Weak and tired as he felt, Simon was determined that he would hold to hope.

They were moving so slowly now. Their careful steps and slow movements reminded Simon of two decrepit invalids. He was glad the ship's rocking had smoothed out more. He realized that neither of them would have the strength to endure another storm.

At the other hatch at last, their shouting took on the desperation of their fears. Simon heard his own screams echo through his head, the wailing of a lunatic, stripped of any pride or pretense. This was his life he cried out for now. "Help! Hey! Help us!" Each word came out raw and frantic. It was a terrifying sound.

But their yelling produced no results. Simon gave his throat permission to rest and hung from the railing, listening.

There were noises on deck above them. Machines were working. Some banging and scraping kind of sounds came now and then, too. Simon wondered if deckhands were manning machines to chip away at the rust. Marc had told them that the task of chipping rust was a never-ending chore. Marc and the unlicensed crewmembers had spent many hours of every day fighting back the rust spots.

Wesley fell silent now, too. They were both quiet, trying hard to listen and decipher the noises and when Wesley finally broke the silence, Simon startled.

"We could try over by those pipes where we were hiding," Wesley ventured. "Remember we heard voices when we were over there. Maybe our voices would carry up to someone better over there?"

Simon nodded his assent. He remembered hearing the muffled sounds of voices while they'd been in port somewhere. When had that been? It seemed so long ago. Back then he had been frightened only that the hold doors would open, and they'd be found. He'd held himself still and uncomfortable for long hours just in case a crewmember came through the hatch, down this ladder. He'd dreaded being caught over all else.

His thirst and a desperate will to survive had changed that, and now he longed to see the hatch open. He wanted to be heard, and discovered. He wanted to at least see the sun again, and get a drink of water before he died.

His mind tortured him with visions of water. He pictured the cold abundance of a rushing river, clear deep lakes and glassfuls of pure clean water. Had he ever appreciated water fully before this time? In spite of the torment it brought, Simon imagined swallowing gulp after gulp of water. Pouring more, he felt liquid spill on his hands and run down his cheek as he drank, savoring the wet luxury of it in his mouth.

It took a good deal longer to get to and then navigate the area of pipes to find the spot where they had hidden. Simon feared several times that one of them would fall. Their steps were not as sure, their muscles not as dependable as they had been over a week ago. Dust still lay thick almost everywhere they touched, and when they gathered enough strength to begin hammering and shouting, thick clouds of the dusty silt fell onto them, drying out their mouths, clogging their noses and choking down into their throats and lungs.

Simon took no pains to remain unseen behind the pipes this time. Neither of them had enough strength to hold tight to keep from slipping down either so they perched on a more stable metal strut, out in the open above a giant pipe, while they alternated resting and listening with shouting and banging.

Wesley had forgotten to shut off his flashlight. Simon stared into the yellow beam capturing the rain of dust, and thought about reminding Wesley of the need to conserve their flash light batteries. He didn't though. Batteries no longer seemed important.

No longer a thing that could be measured, time had ceased to be important. Simon didn't bother looking at his watch anymore. When they both left the area of the pipes and Simon led the way back to the lighted hatch once more, he hadn't the smallest inkling of how much time had passed. Had it been a day? Maybe two days? Or had it been only several hours?

Neither of them had enough energy to scream out for help any longer. They crouched together, simply waiting and listening. When the machine that sounded like a small airplane stopped or when the annoying hum like a dentist's drill seemed to be closer or when one of them imagined footsteps, Simon would hammer frantically against the hatch until his arms failed him.

At one point, Wesley started humming," Nearer My God to Thee, Nearer to Thee."

Simon closed his eyes and listened, shaping his cracked lips around the words he remembered so well. He opened his mouth to voice the words of the next verse, but his mouth was so dry that it took a moment to make any sound at all.

Wesley began singing out the words with Simon on the next verse; not the strong mellow tones that usually distinguished Wesley's voice, but a thin feeble whispery sound.

When a choking cough ended Wesley's singing, Simon stared at the side of Wesley's face that he could see in the bulb light near the hatch. It was a face of death. Wesley's eye sockets had sunk into his head and dark circles had appeared around the blue color of his eyes.

Simon had to look away. His chest felt tight. His eyes burned.

Into the space of silence around them, Simon began singing the words of the song that now meant so much. He placed the words between them like a gift. "A song we sing, a song like no other. It's about Jesus. He is alive . . ." The words were so real now.

Wesley's voice joined his again, blending familiarly. "I know when he comes; I'll see Him in His glory . . ."

They had sung this song together over ten years ago at the beginning of their friendship, and Simon thought it appropriate that they were singing it together now, at the end of their time together.

When their singing faded away, they talked. Memories of their homes and their families, the things closest to their hearts poured out from each of them. They spoke about their faith, too. Wesley mentioned the rain that had fallen on their container in the shipyard. He called it a miracle.

Simon licked his dry lips almost tasting the drops and remembering the sound of those huge splats of rain. Then he said, "You know, you're right. It was a miracle. The rain came every day during the hottest hours of the day. We might have roasted alive without it."

"Cooling rain," Wesley murmured. "I didn't even thank God for that one."

Simon nodded, and paused to thank God himself.

"Being placed where we could get out of our container was a miracle too," Wesley added. "We could have been placed at the bottom of the hold, with containers up tight all around us."

Simon agreed with another nod. After a few moments of silence he added, "That square hole we cut for breathing was a miracle, too. I saw underneath a few containers where there are thick beams of steel under the wood evenly spaced down the length of the box." Simon stopped to shake his head. "Just think if I had cut through the wood only to hit one of those steel beams."

Wesley's mouth opened in thought. Then he whispered. "We would have given up," he said. "We would have stopped sawing the hole . . . and with no air coming in. . ."

"I don't think it was just luck that we picked that spot to saw through for our breathing hole," Simon said.

"No – I don't believe in luck," Wesley said.

"God has been with us," Simon replied.

216

To emphasize his last statement, Simon began telling Wesley about some of the miracles that he had experienced during his escape from Romania to Italy. Wesley hadn't heard about the whole adventure, and Simon drew some reassurance now from remembering how God had been with him.

God had saved him so many times. Shouldn't Simon trust Him now?

Prayer had become a haven for Simon as time passed. His mind began speaking to God so often that most of his thoughts now were merely parts of prayers, an ongoing conversation to his heavenly Father. From his earlier pleading and bargaining prayers, Simon had slipped gradually into questioning prayers. "Why God?" he asked. "Why did you provide so many miracles for me and bring me so far to end like this? I escaped from the army because I would not be able to worship you there. I wanted to live for you always. How will my life serve you if it ends like this? Is this end the price I have to pay for wanting to be free? Is this what you want, God?"

Not for a moment did Simon doubt the existence of God, but doubt tempted him to wonder if perhaps his insignificant life might be too small a matter of consideration for the mighty Lord of the universe.

At other times the events of his life paraded in front of him. He agonized over his mistakes, and let surges of regret wash over and over his tired body, remembering things he had done that he wished he had made right. Unkind things that he had said to his mother and father haunted him now, and he longed for one more moment with each of them to express his love, and to ask forgiveness.

Mistakes that he had made, words that he had spoken in anger he would have done anything to take them back. "Please Lord," he prayed, "Don't let them remember me for that."

The thought that he might never see his family again, to hug his sisters, to hear his mother's voice, to sing once more with his brother, Stefan. His mind tortured him more than his thirst and his aching body as he let himself imagine how his family would react when they found out that he had died.

He hated to think of what he would be putting his family through and how his death would change their lives. He could picture his mother's cry of anguish. He could see his brother's face, contorted with grief.

Only Stefan knew what Simon had done. He'd be worrying now, wondering, hoping for Simon's call. Simon's death in the hull of this ship would be devastating to Stefan.

"God, am I right with you?" Simon prayed. "Am I ready? Please, I need your peace, your assurance. God, can you hear me? I'm afraid."

Chapter 22

Another Miracle

Wesley prayed continually now, too. Words to songs were his constant companions; familiar friends that held up his faith. His humming provided a backdrop to surround the pleas that went heavenward.

His thoughts traveled back again and again to his family. How it would hurt his family when they heard what had happened to him. He hated to think of it. As he envisioned each of them grieving for him, a heavy pain sat cold and hard around his heart, a solid mass of ice that wouldn't melt or dislodge. If only he could embrace them each just once more. If only he could tell them how precious each of them was to him.

Over and over the events of Wesley's life came into review as well. In a few hours when he fell asleep for the last time, he would wake to the second coming. Had he lived a life worthy of awaking to the sight of his Lord? His life and his actions appeared dismal, his heart deceitful. Could God accept him? In the light of eternity, concerns that had occupied his mind just weeks ago seemed trivial now. Nothing was of consequence except his standing in the sight of Jesus. Fighting against his fear and the accusations of his unworthy feelings, Wesley drove back all uncertainties by claiming the promises he had kept in his heart.

His faith plunged in doubt several times, as Wesley fought to accept his circumstances. His prayers remained strong, but hope, like a trapped moth, flung itself futilely against the cage of fear encircling his thoughts. He had felt so sure that God would intervene. If God truly cared, as Wesley knew He did, and if God was watching, as Wesley knew He was, why had He abandoned them to this fate?

Then, just as sure, answers would dispel his doubts. God was here. Wesley could feel His peace, and His comforting presence as he clutched the surety with a stillness that could only have been a divine gift. He didn't want to die; he could not yet accept that his life would end this way. He had wanted it to mean something to make a difference. But Jesus was here. Jesus would never leave him. And with his Savior beside him, Wesley knew he could handle whatever happened. "A song we sing, a song like no other," the voice in his head sang on. "I can trust that He will see me through."

Wesley had stopped climbing the ladder to take his turn smashing the hammer against the hatch. His arms were too weak now and they could barely hold him steady on the narrow steps where he and Simon rested.

He knew that he and Simon had been up there, waiting by the hatch for a very long time, but his internal clock had stopped functioning. He wasn't sure if Simon had been up there for several hours, or perhaps a day or more. He'd calculated some time ago that it had been more than a week since he'd last tipped the water bottle to his mouth to wet his dry tongue and lips. Had that been before or after the storm? Wesley shook his head, trying to clear the stupor threatening to take over, but shaking his head brought an uncomfortable feeling of vertigo. He kept his eyes looking forward and forced his mind away from thoughts of tumbling to

220

the bottom of the ship. He was afraid to let go, even to shift positions.

As he often did now, Wesley dreamed about the sky above the hold. What did it look like right now? Was it full of stars against the royal blue of deepening night? Or was it mid day? Was the sun shining, slanting out from a blanket of cloud cover? Did blue infinity stretch from every horizon? Perhaps there were bright white clouds, rearranging themselves into remarkable shapes. Wesley longed to see this one more time. The yearning to stand beneath the open sky felt just as intense as his desire for water to drink.

When Simon got up once more to take hold of the ladder, Wesley almost said something. His mouth wanted to call out, "Just rest, Simon," or even, "Be careful, Simon." But by the time his mind had created the thought and his mouth had prepared the words, Simon was already on the top step. Everything seemed to be happening in slow motion. Simon's movements, Wesley's disjointed thoughts, even the words of the songs in Wesley's head chugged sluggishly on slow speed.

The clamorous noise of Simon's hammering against the hatch startled Wesley out of his muffled haze. It rang down through the steel plating his head rested against, and sent pain into his head, spurring him to pray once more.

"Please God. Send someone to this hatch. Let them hear us this time," Wesley pleaded. From watching Simon's actions, Wesley knew that this might be the last time Simon would be able to bang against the hatch.

After some time had passed, Wesley heard Simon's voice calling out for help. It was a thin, brokenhearted sound, and it jarred against Wesley more painfully than the ring of the hammer against the metal door. Repeated over and over, the sound of his friend's desperation ripped loose a few choking sobs from somewhere deep inside Wesley's own pain.

When Simon returned to sit next to Wesley, they talked together about happy times. Bicycles and scooters they had owned, came into the conversation. Soccer matches played with friends on summer evenings prompted smiles in their voices. Like two foreigners who were trapped in an alien land, they let their familiar stories to each other confirm who they had been, where they had come from, what they believed.

Wesley made Simon chuckle describing the three jovial guys who had tried to persuade him to go along with them in a container the first time he had met Rica. He reminded Simon of some of the girls they had both known back in Romania. He reminisced about some of his school day pranks and adventures.

He no longer tantalized Simon with the favorite subject of what they would eat first once they were free; a subject they had discussed a week or so ago. He didn't engage Simon in talking about the type of keyboard he planned to buy with his first pay check. Talk didn't include what type of truck or car they might purchase anymore. Neither of them spoke of what type of work they might get or even who they would phone and what they would say to family members once they stepped on dry land. Resignation flavored Wesley's words now. They were the words of an elderly person whose life lay behind him. They were reminiscing thoughts and backward glimpses. Memory seasoned every word. The future no longer existed.

Had Simon accepted the fact that they were not going to survive this ordeal, Wesley wondered? He watched Simon's dark eyes blinking in the semi darkness. Colors barely existed in this darkened hold, but he had noticed that Simon's deep brown eyes had lost some of their lively sparkle. In the light at the top of the ladder Wesley had glimpsed an alarming absence of life. Age seemed to have snuck in to change his friend's face.

Wesley's mind rebelled at such a look at the inevitable. He hadn't voiced his dismal thoughts about their chances for survival to Simon. Was he secretly wishing that Simon still clung to hope? Or was he longing only to protect Simon from such ominous thoughts?

To cheer himself and his silent companion, Wesley said, "We should be getting close to our destination. Canada maybe."

"Maybe," Simon agreed amicably.

After a time, talking became too difficult for Wesley and he felt his voice dry up and stop. Simon took over then. He talked once more about some of the close calls he'd encountered two years ago on his harrowing journey into Italy. The miracles Simon spoke of convicted Wesley's heart and built up his faith. Words about God's love and care were bright threads of embroidery in a rich tapestry of comfort. Simon's voice wove them both snugly in a cocoon of warmth and assurance as he talked. The stories knit them together, connecting them with reminders of the faith they both shared and the life they had both lived.

Wesley concentrated on Simon's words to focus his scrambled thoughts and then, quite suddenly, Wesley realized that Simon was no longer speaking. He hadn't been speaking for some time. An uneasy surprise nudged Wesley from his daze. When had Simon stopped talking? Had he ended his last story?

Wesley felt shakiness in his muscles and a new pain deep in his side. An alarming wooziness swirled specks of color to the backs of his eyes when he moved his head. The blackness around him had thickened, too. Or else it had become harder to breathe. Part of it seemed to catch in his throat each time he sucked in more air.

It was time, he thought.

With great effort Wesley shifted his position and turned his body to face Simon. "We should go back," he said. "Back to the container."

He didn't have to say more. There seemed to be no need to explain why it would be better if they had a place to lie down as they approached the final moments of their lives. Why mention that falling asleep on their familiar hard beds within the container might be a more dignified end? Why speak about the fact that one of them would soon grow too weak to move or hold on any longer? Or that it would be heart wrenching to watch if one of them plunged to the bottom of the ship, leaving the other alone and unable to help.

Wesley felt like someone who had suffered a prolonged illness as he rose to his feet. As he took a few faltering steps he felt that every muscle in his body had wasted away. He had to reach out to hold the wall to stay upright.

When Simon acknowledged, and then carefully stepped over the tools and the packs holding everything else they owned, Wesley paused. Simon had nothing in his hand except the narrow blue plastic flashlight.

He was leaving everything behind. Their wallets with pictures of their families, the music tapes, the camera, money, the Bible that had traveled all the way from Romania and their change of clean clothing.

Wesley took in a ragged breath of stale cold air with the realization of what leaving their packs behind really meant. Nothing in Simon's eyes or in Wesley's trembling movements had spoken more clearly. It wasn't because the return trip would be too difficult to manage with things to carry, although that was true. It was simply because they would not need any of these things anymore. They weren't going to Canada or even above deck to feel the sun on their faces. They weren't going to make it.

No words needed to be spoken about the decision. Wesley hardly had the strength to experience regret as the pang of defeat felt too immense to comprehend.

Slowly, carefully, Wesley stepped wide around the chisel and the hammer and his own familiar packsack of belongings. Like a wounded soldier helping his wounded comrade to the first aid tent, Wesley shuffled and staggered along, one moment holding to Simon for support, and another reaching out to support Simon. It was slow going. Hours passed while they staggered and rested and shuffled with baby steps.

Crossing the beam had to be done cautiously. Wesley had little opportunity to feel frightened this time. Once or twice during the course of their passage back, Wesley wondered if he would have enough strength to reach their container. He wondered, too, if falling might be a quicker, easier end. If he had been alone, it might have been. Now though, he realized that if he fell to a quick death here, it would only make things more painful for Simon.

Wesley felt grateful that the containers were no longer slamming back and forth within their steel struts. His hands were no longer strong enough or his fingers quick enough to avoid being smashed between the containers and their upright fencing.

A sigh of relief shuddered through his body when they finally stood beside the jagged hole in their container. Summoning up the last snippets of energy, he climbed inside struggling to lift his body away from the jagged metal.

He lay still then, trying to bring air into his lungs, waiting for his limbs to stop trembling with fatigue. He was so tired. He knew he might not wake again if sleep took him now, but he longed for it anyway. Closing his eyes, Wesley reached out once more to his God.

But Simon still had not started to climb inside the container. With a groan of effort Wesley pulled himself into a sitting position once more and peered out, searching for Simon in the black gloom.

With the flashlight's dim glow, Wesley could just make out the darker form of his friend standing in the shadowy darkness on the container beside theirs. His shoulders were level with the hole in the container, close enough to touch. His head was turned away from Wesley, looking up to where he pointed the beam of his flashlight.

"Simon, come in," Wesley said. His voice came out in a hoarse raspy whisper. With another grunt of exertion, Wesley turned his flashlight beam down to capture Simon's face.

"I see a light," Simon told him. His eyes were wide like the startled eyes of a wild animal. They had changed from the quiet listless stare Wesley had seen the last time he looked at his friend. These eyes had movement and life.

"There's a light around the rusty hatch. I see a light," Simon repeated. His voice sounded raspy too, but it had a sudden urgency that alarmed Wesley. Simon was probably hallucinating, Wesley thought. He had heard that people who were sick or dying often saw things that weren't there.

"Can you see it from there?" Simon asked. "Look. Just look!"

At the startling quiver in Simon's voice something turned over inside Wesley with a lurch of pain that stung his eyes. He could not bear the terrible radiance of sudden hope that shone in Simon's face and came out in his words. How could he tell Simon that it was time to let go? Where would he find the words to let Simon see that they were both too weak to do anything more? Don't do this anymore Simon, he wanted to cry. Everything that we could try, we tried, he wanted to say, but he had no heart for the words. Instead, with as much kindness as he could muster, Wesley said, "Just come inside."

The words and what they meant and even the sound of the waver in his own voice bumped up against a raw place of hurt that he tried to push down deep where he couldn't touch it again. His whole body ached from the strain as he leaned out to look at Simon. Every muscle cried out for rest. He couldn't climb that steep narrow ladder again. He was too weak. Too tired. Simon probably could not manage that climb again either and it would be a futile attempt anyway. Simon must know that as well as Wesley.

"Simon. Please," Wesley pleaded. "Just come inside."

"No, no, Wesley, just look up there. Look! There is a light," Simon insisted.

Wesley closed his eyes to still the pounding in his head. His entire body implored him to lie back and surrender, but his mind hesitated. He knew Simon; if Simon imagined he saw a light, he wouldn't let it go. If Simon had somehow grasped onto another thread of hope, he would push himself to make an effort against all reason. Wesley couldn't let him go off alone. Despite his weakness, and no matter how pointless, Wesley could not let his best friend embark upon another stab at survival on his own. What if Simon fell? What if his tired body betrayed his determined spirit and he had to lie down half way there to breathe his last breaths alone? Wesley could not bear such a thought. No, they would stay together. They had been through too much to separate now.

Wesley knew that it was impossible for any light to come through that small-unused hatch. Every time they had made the climb to hammer against that rusty hatch, Wesley had been more and more convinced that the door was not operational. No one had opened or used that entry into the hold for a very long time. The thick dusty coating of grime on the ladder attested to the fact, but there was no use in arguing those facts with Simon. Just thinking through the dispute seemed to require more energy than Wesley could summon. He would have to crawl back out. He would have to indulge Simon's perceived vision of light and at least stand out there beside his friend to look up.

Wesley handed Simon the flashlight. He didn't bother turning it off anymore. Saving the batteries wasn't something either of them spoke of now as both lights had dimmed into a weak yellow glow.

Carefully, treating each limb as a fragile artifact that might crumble with rough handling, Wesley began to pull himself out of the hole. He would have fallen if Simon hadn't helped him wiggle out and drop the few feet down onto the container beside theirs. It took a great deal longer than the first time he had climbed out of the box.

He stood finally holding to Simon's shoulder to steady his shaky body. A swirling blackness behind his eyes threatened to topple him.

"There," Simon persisted. Simon pushed at Wesley to make him move over to look past a tall tower of containers. He pointed up through the window on the wall around the tiny platform surrounding the hatch. "Look. There is a thin line of light coming through. As if the hatch were opened."

Wesley tipped his head and stared in the direction that Simon pointed. His heart gave a tiny jump and landed in his throat. A feeling of hope he only half remembered crowded in to fill up his chest.

There was a light, Simon was not imagining things. Wesley could see it too. A knife blade slice of light showed on one side of the metal door. The hatch was open.

Chapter 23

Divine Intervention

Simon wasn't sure he or Wesley would have the strength to get up to the rusty hatch again. This door in the ceiling of the hold was much closer to their container than the other lighted hatch, and there was no dangerous beam to cross this time, but they were both so weak they could hardly walk. Together they lurched along, leaning out for support on each other. Several times they resorted to crawling, and they had to stop to rest every few breaths. The prospect of light, water and life itself proved to be a powerful elixir though. It kept Simon moving, even after he thought his strength was entirely gone.

Fearful that the light would disappear, Simon kept looking up at it as they worked their way to the ladder. The light remained a sliver of optimism, a slice of brightness so intense that it hardly seemed as though it could be real.

When they finally reached the ladder, Simon left Wesley at the bottom and pulled himself up to the hatch rung by rung. The narrow ladder only had room for one set of feet at a time. At the top Simon took in a deep breath and then pushed against the door. Nothing budged, but almost immediately a shadow passed over the light. The movement spooked him, and he almost lost his grip.

Looking down at Wesley's face, Simon hissed, "I just saw someone walk by." He felt excited and terrified at the same time. "I can see someone out there."

"Yell at him," Wesley shouted up.

Frantically Simon shook his head no. He could hardly make out Wesley's expression in the flashlight's meager glow, but Wesley's shouting scared him. Here, this close to possible rescue, his courage failed him. All the grim stories of the fate of stowaways flew back into his head to frighten him. "I'm afraid," he said. He wasn't sure if Wesley had even heard him.

Squinting into the narrow brightness while turning his head sideways, he tried to make out the shapes of things he could see through the crack of the hatch. It was all so bright. But Simon could see a crewman's feet and orange clad trousers.

"Come down," Wesley was calling to him. "Let me go up."

It took a long time for Wesley to climb the ladder. Simon watched from the bottom until his neck felt too wobbly to hold his head.

"I can't see anyone," Wesley called back. His voice sounded odd and Simon had to force his tired neck to look back up to see if it was really Wesley speaking to him. He cringed as Wesley began to yell. It wasn't a very big sound with other sounds above the deck sounding louder. But Wesley didn't give up, he kept hollering. It felt like a long time. The hatch remained closed except for its tiny slit of light for no one had heard.

For another eon of waiting, Simon stood at the bottom of the ladder, leaning into the grimy metal for support. He looked up when Wesley started slowly back down the ladder.

"I didn't see anything," Wesley said, back on the level with Simon.

"There was someone walking by the hatch," Simon insisted. Once again he climbed to the top of the ladder. He felt determined this time, but he couldn't seem to shake his fear. It felt like a very long time since he had seen or talked with anyone besides Wesley and seemed years ago that he had stood free under a sky full of sunshine.

He used his plastic flashlight to bang against the hatch when he'd used up his voice. Then he stopped to rest and look back down to where Wesley waited. When he looked back at the hatch another shadow crossed the light. Simon inched closer and peered out at the shadow. A crewman. He was wearing orange coveralls. Large black printing on the man's back spelled out CROATIA.

"There's someone working right here!" Simon pointed, but he turned his head to Wesley as he spoke.

"Bang your flashlight again," Wesley ordered. "Yell at him."

Again, terror froze Simon to stillness. He stared down at Wesley's upturned face.

Wesley began pulling himself up the ladder. "We have to get out," he insisted. "Simon, just do it. We're going to die if we don't get some help . . . some water. . ."

The word, die, got Simon's attention. Dying had been a word in their minds, never on their lips. To have the word set loose, acknowledging what they both knew as truth, lent Simon new resolve. He turned his face up to the hatch, peered through the opening of light again, and then yelled. His voice sounded weak and thin.

"Pound with the flashlight," Wesley prompted.

Thump, bump, clank. The sound of Simon's flashlight hitting the metal hatch door pounded into his head.

This time the crewmember turned for he had heard. Simon could see a startled expression in the man's leathery brown face. The man looked afraid, but he was coming closer. He started to bend over for a look at where the sound was coming from, and then abruptly he stood back up again and backed away. Turning, he hollered something over his shoulder. Simon couldn't make out what language the man was using.

231

More shadows appeared, almost blocking the light now. Then Simon heard something happening to the hatch sounding as if bolts were being removed. A high squealing noise erupted, metal on metal.

Simon backed down the ladder, partly to be out of the way as the hatch opened and partly as an automatic reaction to his overwhelming fear. He might have backed all the way down the ladder if it hadn't been for Wesley blocking the way behind him.

Light flooded, in a blinding, excruciating, glorious light. Air flooded in, too, with an odor of color and life.

"Go," Wesley prompted him. "Go up."

Simon couldn't see at all. Hand over hand he ascended, squeezing his eyes against the painful brilliance. He felt a rush of wind on his head, brightness on his face as a blur of orange legs shuffled about him at eye level. Simon squinted at the man who stood closest to him. His eyes began streaming out tears as he blinked against the light, struggling to see. The man was speaking to him, but Simon couldn't understand any of the words. Hand motions were clear however, and the man was motioning for Simon to come up.

So Simon tried. He grasped the solid warmth of the metal hatch and lifted his feet to the last rung of the ladder as he tried to pull his body forward and out. His arms trembled with the effort, his lungs gasped and sucked at the fresh cool air while strong arms pulled him up.

Upright on the deck Simon staggered to gain his balance with a spinning sensation that almost toppled him. Voices chattered at him in some foreign language.

A delicious breeze swept his dirty hair over his face, but it was too much. His legs buckled beneath him.

Wesley had been lifted out now, too. Narrow eyed against the brilliance of light, he had crumpled down to a sitting position as soon as he came above deck. His voice sounded odd as he attempted to answer the men who were speaking to them.

With lilting questions in their speech and lots of hand

232

motions, the crewmen finally got their message across. They wanted to know if there were any more stowaways below. How many, they seemed to be asking.

"Just us," Wesley answered. He was using hand motions, trying to explain. "There are no more. We were the only ones down there."

Simon heard Wesley telling them what language they spoke, "Romanian, and some Italian," Wesley said, but Simon couldn't tell if anyone in their audience of curious listeners had understood. No words sounded familiar to Simon.

When the crewman who seemed to be in charge indicated to Simon that they were to get up and follow him, Simon tried to obey. He managed to stand. He even took a few steps forward, but he couldn't seem to command his limbs properly. He felt ragged and loose as if his joints had come unfastened. He didn't fall when his legs began to buckle this time, however, while two crewmen in orange overalls lifted him to his feet. They held him firmly, one gripping him under each arm as they half steered him and half dragged him along the deck.

To Simon's left, heaps of containers rose in colorful stacks. To his right brilliant turquoise waters ran to the edge of the world. In front of him, far down the length of the long ship, a wall of white rose up with layers of windows. It was all still fuzzy, too brilliant for focusing and too vast to take in all at once.

Simon gave up trying to use his feet after a bit. He let his feet and legs drag dead weight. The men helping him were walking too quickly for his legs to keep up, and he was too weak to keep lifting his feet.

Along with Wesley, Simon was taken to a small room. A tiny wiry man with a smile that took up most of his face brought them some water. Another brought in some fish on buns. The odor alone felt nourishing.

One of the men who had half carried Simon to the room gave Wesley a pat on the back and nodded at Simon with a look of genuine compassion. Another, very young looking crewman gave

Simon thumbs up signal. "Take heart, you'll be okay now", his grin seemed to say. The man who appeared to be in charge herded everyone out of the room and left Simon and Wesley alone inside locking the door as he left.

Simon watched as Wesley drank some water, and then he drank down his own share. As good as the food smelled, water was what he had been craving. There wasn't enough really, hardly enough to quench their thirst. But the blissful wetness in his mouth made him close his eyes and sigh with gratitude. It was wet, life giving water, and the act of kindness shown in bringing it to them seemed hopeful. If they were planning to throw Simon and Wesley overboard, surely they wouldn't bring them water and food and smile at them so encouragingly, would they?

For some time after that, food took their entire concentration. Simon couldn't believe such a simple meal could taste so good. It seemed to take a very long time to chew and swallow. Both he and Wesley felt stuffed when they had eaten only part of what had been given them.

The room they had been locked in was small and rather bare but bright and clean. It felt like a palace compared to where they had been confined for so long. Bunk beds were built against one wall. A corner housed a bathroom complete with a shower and a small sink. An adjacent corner held a table and chairs where Wesley had already collapsed in a stupor. Across from the bunks a round window the size of Simon's head brought in light.

Simon let himself down slowly to sit on the hard flat mattress on the bottom bunk as he stared out at the brightness coming in the tiny window. Even in these modest swells he could hear containers straining against their lashings. The sound was different up here but familiar, too. He waited, listening and worrying about what would happen next.

A stocky fellow with bushy eyebrows and a bushy mustache brought them more drinking water a few minutes later. His name was Paul, he told them. He was the second engineer, and he spoke a little Italian. He smiled reassuringly at them and then wiped his smile away to let them know that the captain would come soon to speak with them.

The man could not stay and talk, but Simon did manage to ask where the ship was heading.

"Quebec," the man answered. "Next stop, Quebec. Two days maybe." Then with a smile and a congenial wave he left them, locking the room from the outside.

"Where is Quebec?" Simon asked Wesley as soon as Paul had left. "Is that in Canada?"

Wesley shrugged. He didn't know either.

It would have been a good time to sleep. The bright warm room rolled back and forth with a steady lullaby of rocking, but Simon couldn't relax.

He still wasn't sure it all was real and hardly knew if he could trust this new situation. Did this welcome turn of events mean they were going to survive? Or were there worse things to come? How would they be punished for what they had done?

For awhile they whispered back and forth, partly because their voices were still scratchy and weak from hollering so much, and partly because they were terrified.

Simon jumped when he heard the sound of the door unlocking and an older, stocky man in an immaculate uniform entered the room.

Captain Minsky, the man introduced himself to them. And who were they? He wanted to know. He looked as if he had just stepped out of a movie about a sea voyage with his white beard, captain's hat and crisp white uniform. For a moment Simon could only stare. When he found his voice, Captain Minsky switched smoothly into speaking Italian to continue, but Simon found it a challenge just to keep up to all the man's questions.

"When did you get on board?" Captain Minsky asked. "How did you get on my ship?" he demanded. "Which port? Are there anymore of you down there?"

Simon answered each question truthfully. He explained as best he could about the container they had entered, but he had no answers to give the captain about names of places and ports.

The captain seemed more intent on finding out how they had come aboard, however. His expressions relaxed some when he learned they had not boarded his ship on foot, but had come aboard in a container. Although Captain Minsky had a business like manner and set Simon's heart to pounding with his barrage of interrogation, he acted quite friendly. He seemed genuinely interested in how Simon and Wesley had managed to survive below deck for most of the passage.

"What did you do during the storm?" he asked. His face crinkled into something almost humorous when he admitted that the storm had been a bad one. "It was a close one," he told them. "Very close."

He chuckled aloud, and his dark blue eyes sparkled with mirth when he discovered that Wesley and Simon had no idea where his ship was heading. "You mean you don't even know where you are going?" he teased. "We are going to Montreal," he told them. "Quebec."

"Canada?" Wesley queried.

Captain Minsky laughed once more. "Yes. Yes. Canada. Do you speak some English? French?"

"No."

"What do you plan to do in Canada?" the captain asked.

Simon shrugged, but he couldn't keep his face from grinning back at the man's teasing grin.

"Why didn't you come up from below before this?" the captain asked next. "Why didn't you come up after we left port in Portugal?"

Simon groped for the words just as Wesley said, "We couldn't."

"The hatch was locked," Simon explained. "We tried to yell and bang, but no one heard. We couldn't get out."

236

"So how did you get up here?" the captain barked in his straightforward manner.

Simon told Captain Minsky about the rusty hatch, about seeing the light and then seeing the crewman working near the hatch.

Captain Minsky threw up his hands and shook his head at them. "Impossible!" he said. "That hatch is never open. Not even a crack. Not that hatch. It has to be kept water-tight. Always. You would never have seen any light from that hatch!" His blue eyes squinted at them suspiciously. Then he shook his head once more. "I've captained this ship for almost 20 years. I know my ship. That hatch has never been opened!"

Simon didn't bother to argue. He and Wesley had both seen the light along the edge of the hatch, but this man who spoke in such a commanding way was the captain of this ship. Instead of responding, Simon stole a glance at Wesley's face. He watched as something like awe traveled over Wesley's mouth and came to rest in his eyes. And he read the words in Wesley's eyes without any difficulty. "Another of God's miracles," they seemed to say.

Without further discussion about the mysterious light that had saved them, Captain Minsky jumped to more questions. He wanted to know exactly what they had brought onto his ship. "What have you got with you?" he asked. When Simon mentioned tools, he barked, "What kind of tools? What type of drill, what kind of knife? "And, "Where are they now?" he wanted to know. "Where was the container they had come aboard in? Can you show me?"

Simon assured the captain that they could see their container from the rusty hatch where they had emerged. His legs were steadier now, he thought, but as soon as he began following the captain out onto the deck his knees betrayed him. Once again two crewmen stepped alongside to help him walk. The sun blinded him and he staggered as he willed his legs to follow the captain's brisk stride.

Retracing their steps towards the bow of the ship, Simon turned to see the little guy with the big smile following behind

Wesley. The bearded man who had first heard them calling from below joined the procession when the captain waved him over.

When the hatch was opened once more, Simon crouched down to look into the hull as the man with the beard shone a powerful light into the hold. "There," Simon directed them, pointing. "Can you see the cut in that container? Below that blue one, see? That is our container;" he told Captain Minsky. Simon offered to go down, but the captain waved away his words.

"Where are your things?" Captain Minsky asked.

It was impossible for Simon to envision, from above deck, where they had left their things at the other hatch. They'd traveled a long distance from their container to get to the hatch where the light shone. At least it had seemed like a long distance. He explained as best he could.

Captain Minsky commanded a few new orders and crewman went running. One crewman was sent down the rusty ladder and minutes later he came back to report.

The captain asked a few more questions and then grunted as he listened. He shook his head disapprovingly at one point, but then admitted that he was impressed they had used plastic bags and bottles for their garbage and body wastes. He seemed mollified that although the container had been damaged, none of the cargo he was responsible for had been ruined.

To reach the other hatch, the lighted hatch where Simon and Wesley had spent so many hours, they had to go down a few stairs until they were partly below the top deck. Simon could see why no one would have heard their cries.

Two crewmen went down the steps to recover Simon and Wesley's possessions.

The sky had lost some of its brightness by this time. The sun hung low close to the water. Simon stared out at the unbelievably immense expanse of water, following the movement of the dark waves as they rolled over and broke to display a smattering of frothy white lace.

His legs and his thoughts moved as if they were strangers who had never met.

Back in the room he muttered his thanks, along with Wesley, as the bearded crewman brought in their packsacks. Simon didn't see where their tools had gone. It didn't matter. He didn't care if he ever saw those tools again.

A tall man in a white shirt, who introduced himself as Michael, brought them more food. He spoke in hesitant Italian to them before he left locking their door from the outside.

The room had dimmed to twilight by now and Wesley went to turn on the light.

The blessing of illumination felt like another gift. Simon looked up to smile, than laughed instead. He pointed at Wesley's face. "You look awful! Look at your face!"

Wesley stood to inspect himself in the little mirror over the sink. He stood there staring for so long, being so quiet, that Simon moved in closer to stand behind him. He met Wesley's eyes in the little white-framed wall mirror.

Wesley's hair had turned several shades darker than normal. It stood up stiff with grime over most of his head coated orangey in spots where he had leaned against rusty pipes. Patterns and lines in his face and neck stood out black with dirt and grease and deep, dark hollows circled his light blue eyes. The clothing he wore had no color at all.

His sweater held all the caked on silt and grime of the hold. It looked as if Wesley wore a dusting rag, used once too often without being washed or shaken.

The biggest shock in the mirror wasn't Wesley's unbelievably dirty face however. The greatest astonishment to Simon was the wild-eyed stranger standing behind Wesley.

239

Chapter 24

First Sight of Canada

It was Wesley's turn to snicker now as Simon stared at himself in the mirror.   As Simon shook his head in disbelief, Wesley let amusement bubble up from his throat. The sound of his laughter sounded so curious that he kept on giggling long after Simon's face had stopped appearing so funny, just to listen to the way laughter sounded.

How long had it been since he had laughed?

Wesley had planned to give in to sleep when they returned to their room. He sighed with longing at the blanket on the mattress and the clean white cased pillow. But now that he had seen himself, he knew he wanted a shower and some soap before he would let himself sleep.

Wesley waited while Simon took the first shower. Then he stood long under the raining warmth letting the soap and water rinse the grime from his hair and his body, letting the soothing feel of moisture plump out his skin and encase him in luxury.

It was as if his body had been craving a drink too, and he had to force himself to finally turn off the water.

Wesley washed his bag next, and all the clothing he had been wearing. It took some time in the small sink, but he felt better when the job was complete. Simon had done the same, and soon all the clothing they had been wearing hung dripping all over the room.

He didn't remember falling asleep. The brightness that slanted into their room the next morning only slightly penetrated his consciousness. He had a hazy awareness of the morning being already late, but he hugged tight the comfort of sleep, reluctant to come awake.

Simon's voice interrupted his dreams. "Wesley, get up. We've been invited to go out to eat with the crew," Simon told him.

It was true. Their door had been unlocked. Paul, the second engineer who had announced the captain's arrival the day before, had come to take them to the dining room.

It wasn't far and Wesley could hear the dining hall before they came to it. Loud music blared out from the room with the words and the tune sounding foreign. Wesley followed Paul hesitantly; suddenly shy as at least six or seven crewmembers looked up to watch them enter.

He grinned back and waved when he spotted the man who had brought them food the day before. The tall fellow, who had introduced himself as Michael, was wearing an apron as he came out of the galley. A dark skinned man with a steaming plate of something that looked a bit like bacon had stopped to speak with Simon. He was the cook, Michael told Wesley. It sounded as though he was asking Simon about what they would like to eat. Wesley could hear Simon explaining that neither of them ate pork.

All around them, curious crewmembers stared, but they all appeared friendly. One man with a scarred face stood up to nod congenially. Another rose to shake Wesley's hand. Paul gestured them towards a place to sit, and told them they should sit down.

Wesley took his seat gratefully. He felt surprised at the crew's behavior and nothing could have prepared him for such hospitable treatment. As the crew members each stopped to wave or smile or acknowledge Wesley and Simon, and as Michael and another man in an apron hurried to serve them both with food and rushed to refill their juice, Wesley felt more like some type of celebrity than a criminal.

No one bothered to lock the door behind them when they got back to their room. A crewmember, who had smiled at them in the dining room motioned to them at the window, holding up paper and a pen. Wesley realized the man was asking if they would like to have paper to write letters.

"Yes," Simon answered quickly. "We can write letters to our families," he exclaimed.

Paul came back later to give them a short tour, stopping to let them peek into the engine room, and introduced them to the games room where he told them they would be welcome to pick a book, play table tennis or select a movie to watch from a cupboard full of video cassettes. Wesley stood staring like a small child looking at a toy box full of new playthings.

In the dining room at the next meal Wesley had to hold up his hands and shake his head as one and then another brought more food for them or offered a variety of special treats. His eyes opened in astonishment as a soup bowl heaped with ice cream was placed in front of him.

It was as if he and Simon were new pets to these men, exotic, and rather frail curiosities and in need of much spoiling and coddling in order to survive.

Wesley couldn't help but worry though, about what might happen to them once they arrived in port. Wesley knew the crewmen, and even Captain Minsky, would have no say in determining their fate once he and Simon disembarked. Would they be sent back to Romania? Split up and locked in a prison cell?

"No use worrying," Simon told him, reading his mind. They were out on the deck with the wind on their faces, "Unless you think we should jump overboard and escape," he laughed.

Laughter still sounded odd in Wesley's ears. He grinned back at Simon and said, "Whatever happens, at least we did get to see the sun again." He took in a deep lung full of fresh air and closed his still sensitive eyes against the brightness. Holding tight to the railing he stood into the wind and blinked until he could squint against the sunshine. He stared down as the waves tumbled into froth meeting the port side of the ship. The water was such an intense, beautiful blue that it made Wesley's teeth ache.

When Paul arrived to stand next to them he told them that they were nearing the coast of Canada. Wesley squinted in the direction he pointed.

Many crewmembers were gazing in the same direction hungry for that first sight of land. Everyone seemed to be eager to be the first one to spot it. Wesley couldn't see anything different about the horizon, when someone finally called out, "Land!" He smiled back along with Simon when a workman pointed and grinned, though, wanting somehow to share in the excitement of the moment. It was easy to smile and catch the crew's enthusiasm, but anxiety knotted Wesley's stomach. Worry collided with hope tangling into an all too familiar knot of apprehension.

He saw the same worry in Simon's eyes. "You'll be all right," Paul told them, sensing their concern.

A crewman stopped to slap Simon on the shoulder good-naturedly. "Canada is a good country. A good place," he repeated, to reassure them.

Wesley appreciated the words of optimism, but he wasn't convinced. The crewmen offering the reassuring words weren't even Canadian. They hadn't committed a criminal offence or been caught trying to enter the country illegally. They didn't know what would happen to the stowaways.

For a long time there was not much to see on the barely visible shoreline, but Wesley and Simon were too excited for a glimpse of their new home to leave the railing. When the engines switched from a thrumming tenor to a slower, deeper baritone the outlines of small towns and then bigger centers and cities crept into the horizon.

"We've slowed down," Wesley said. "Maybe we're getting ready to dock." A flock of butterflies flapped about inside him.

An officer had come to take their photos the morning after they'd been rescued from the hold. Through Paul, acting as an interpreter, Wesley and Simon were told that their pictures would be emailed ahead to customs. They had been warned that immigration officials would come on board to escort them off the ship as soon as the ship docked in Montreal. Paul had explained to them that they would have to be locked in their room as soon as they arrived. He told them the rules required that any stowaways had to be confined.

Soon the increasingly amazing sights on the shore distracted them from worry, and they both gawked in wonder. Around them barges chugged by, churning brown waters into foamy lather. Tugboats looked like toys maneuvering ahead of them. Bridges sparkled in the sunset. On land, unbelievably wide highways swarmed with trucks and buses and sleek shining cars, all the size of children's toys at this distance. Closer to shore, boats of every size lined marinas, and lights from windowed buildings winked in the twilight. Gantry cranes hovered like dinosaurs waiting to feed in wide flat shipyards. It was noisy, busy and too overwhelming to absorb.

The ship's engines thumbed down once more.

"We're in a river now," Simon said. "The St. Lawrence seaway."

"You've been getting geography lessons I see," Wesley observed.

"Paul told me," Simon admitted. "There's a speed limit and everything." Abruptly Simon pointed towards shore. "Look! Look at that truck."

Wesley looked. Traffic was thick on the highway paralleling the seaway, but Wesley knew just which truck Simon had spotted. It was a huge hauling truck carrying two containers, but it wasn't like any of the flat-faced trucks they were used to seeing in Europe. It had a protruding nose of shiny metal. "Just like in the movies," Wesley said. It was the only place he had ever seen such trucks. He nudged Simon and pointed at a school bus because the yellow bus was something else he had never seen except in the movies. "Do you see the bus? The yellow school bus?" he shouted.

"Just like the movies," Simon repeated.

"Do you think this is Montreal?" Wesley asked.

Simon shrugged his lack of knowledge. "Montreal or Quebec,"

Simon said. "I think Paul said it was Quebec, but there were many cities along the St Lawrence sea-way." Without looking at Wesley, Simon added. "I guess we should be in our room."

Wesley nodded. But neither of them moved.

They were still staring when Paul found them.

"The Captain wanted me to see you to your room," Paul said. "I'm supposed to lock the door before the customs people come aboard. The immigration officials might not get here until morning now, but I'm supposed to see you to your room anyway." Paul looked almost apologetic as he escorted them back to the room and then left, locking the door.

When Michael arrived with food, Wesley's nerves were so tight that he knew his stomach would not welcome the late supper.

"Relax," Michael told them. "Eat. Get some sleep."

They both tried to eat, but neither of them could swallow much. Although Wesley tried to find sleep, he felt he was only skimming the surface of dreams when he closed his eyes. Before dawn Simon got up and dressed and began pacing the room restlessly. Wesley sat up on his bunk with his chin in his hands.

Nothing had changed, he thought. Perhaps they had only made things worse for themselves. They were in a new country now, yes. But they were still illegal immigrants. They had paid a high price for a freedom that might never be claimed. Had they been better off in Italy, hiding, worrying? What had they really accomplished? Being deported back to Romania was still a distinct possibility. They were still eligible for prison time and military duty there.

They were prisoners, at the mercy of authorities who could detain them in prison here or send them back to Romania to be punished for their behavior. The authorities would be arriving any time now.

Chapter 25

Welcome to Canada

Simon tried to tell himself reassuring things as he paced the small cabin, waiting for the immigration officials.

They had been well treated here on this ship with his fears about being thrown overboard had been wasted worries. Perhaps he was wasting time worrying now as well? He couldn't erase the memories of his own experiences in Italy or forget the tales of mistreatment he had heard. He knew of many who had attempted to emigrate, who had been immediately deported. His own horrific interrogation after his capture in Italy kept rushing back into his mind to torment him, too. He had no reason to believe that being taken into custody here, in a different land, would be any better.

When Paul and another ship's officer arrived to escort them from their room, Simon had worked himself into a sweat. His entire body tingled with fear.

"Bring all your things," Paul told them. "Your packsacks, wallets... Bring everything."

Simon grabbed up his things and watched Wesley fumble with the straps on his packsack. Wesley's face looked as scared as

Simon felt. Even Paul looked serious and apprehensive, Simon thought. His usual smile and good-natured banter had been replaced with a grim silence.

Their footsteps pounded out an even rhythm as their procession climbed to the captain's office on the top floor of the accommodations tower. Simon looked only to the next metal stair and concentrated on lifting one foot and then the other. No one spoke. Simon thought perhaps even Paul could not find a cheerful word for the occasion.

They followed solemnly as Paul led them down a long, narrow hallway and then stood aside for them to enter a room that appeared to be an office. Captain Minsky sat waiting for them behind an enormous, dark wood desk. A balding man with piercing black eyes stepped toward them and said something in a language Simon couldn't understand. Beside him, a broad shouldered man in uniform stood with his hands behind his back. A woman in a dark uniform spoke to them in Romanian.

"Welcome to Canada," she said. To Simon's ears the words were a mockery. They couldn't really mean welcome. Why would they say such a thing? He and Wesley had arrived here illegally; they had committed a crime. He didn't think for one moment that anyone in that room meant that they were really welcome to Canada. The sound of his native tongue felt almost heartening though. Simon watched as Wesley turned his face towards the familiar Romanian language as the woman asked each of them if they required a doctor.

In spite of her surprising words of welcome and her question about their needs for a doctor, however, the woman was all business. She did not even seem to be looking at them, but watched the balding man, and spoke after he did. "Face forward," she told them. "You are to stand here," she instructed. "Place your hands down here on the desk. Spread your legs," she ordered. "You are not to speak to me. I am an interpreter only. I will not answer any questions. You will direct all responses to this man."

Every muscle tightened as Simon obeyed. He felt hands searching his body.

"Where are your wallets?" the woman asked. "Where is your identification?"

Wesley told her that their wallets were inside their packs.

Handcuffs were placed about their wrists next, and within minutes they were being guided out of the office and down the stairway.

Simon looked around him this time. He felt surprised at the view. It was an incredible distance to the ship's deck from this height.

Surprise found him again when they reached the end of the stairs for the crew, and even Captain Minsky, had lined up there to say good bye to them. Smiling faces grinned encouragement as hands lifted 'thumbs up' gestures in gifts of optimism. Some familiar faces called out words of support or offered friendly waves.

Simon felt his heart clench down in gratitude to these men who had been so kind.

When they had descended the long gangplank off the ship, he looked back wondering if anyone would be watching or waving. There were no crewmen to see so instead, Simon opened his mouth in amazement at the incredible length of the ship he and Wesley had ridden across the ocean. He'd had no idea the container ship had been so enormous, and he almost stumbled as his eyes tried to find each end of the vessel.

But there were wonders all about them now. From the back of the caged compartment of the mini van where he and Wesley were seat belted against each wall, Simon could see a whole new world. He swiveled his head one way and then the other way, trying to see everything as the little Chevy Ventura drove into an increasingly demanding maze of busy streets and tall buildings.

His heart dropped into his stomach when the van turned into an underground parking lot. Something he could only figure must have been a thread of hope extinguished inside of him as a barred metal gate clanged shut behind the van. Always alert for a chance to flee, Simon had never stopped planning how and when they might break free. Would escape be possible from a fortress such as this?

Police photographs were taken in a bright office like room, and both Simon and Wesley were fingerprinted. A long series of elevators, hallways, surveillance cameras and uniformed persons speaking the curious sounding French language greeted them next. Simon was so busy looking around that he didn't notice when Wesley was guided down a different hallway. The sudden and shocking absence of his friend frightened him even more than the stark interrogation room in which he was placed to wait. Wesley had been by his side for so many weeks now, with him through so many trials, that his absence made Simon feel horribly alone and exposed.

The questions started a few moments later when a thin faced officer and another darker skinned man entered the room. The man with the sharply angled nose and jaw rattled off questions in a booming loudspeaker voice while the man with darker skin and short curly hair interpreted in Romanian.

"Who are you? What is your full complete name? Where are you from? How did you get here? Why did you leave your country? When did you leave? When did you arrive? Have you ever been charged with a criminal offence? Where did you complete your schooling? Where is your family? What do they do for a living? Who is with you? What is his complete name? What is your relationship to each other? How did you meet? Why have you come to Canada? Do you have family here in Canada?"

On and on the interrogation continued. Even the dreaded, "Where is your ID? Why have you no identification papers?" came into the barrage of questioning. Simon almost flinched with that question, remembering the black gloves that lashed out to sting across his face in Italy. Although the narrow faced man acted angry and spoke abruptly, he made no move to hit Simon. He assaulted only with words. His questions went on and on, coming so quickly that the interpreter had difficulty keeping up, and Simon had to struggle to respond in a timely manner.

Hours later, when Simon thought perhaps he had answered everything the man wanted to know about him, the questions began again. Many of them were the same questions that he had already answered disguised in a different assortment of words. Queries were shaped in new sentences hidden subtly in a confusing wordplay, but they were often the same queries.

Even if he'd been tempted to lie in an attempt to prompt leniency, Simon didn't think he would be smart enough to dupe these interrogation experts. Honesty is always the best choice, he remembered learning. Just tell the truth, he told himself. So he answered truthfully coming clean with every detail.

None of his answers seemed satisfactory though. No matter how often he repeated the same answers, the man with the loud voice was not appeased. Simon didn't know if he was being forced to continue answering the same kind of questions over and over because he wasn't answering them correctly or if the questions went on and on just to wear him down or try to trip him up.

Tense with apprehension, Simon focused intently on the thin man's face as each question was hurled out at him. He faced the interpreter as the foreign demands were untangled into Romanian words. On the table in front of him Simon's fists tightened and loosened and clenched again as he struggled to keep up to the man's rapid questions.

When his interrogator produced Simon's wallet and laid it on the table, Simon wasn't sure what was happening. He watched as the man removed each picture and each scrap of folded paper. When the wallet was emptied and everything from it had been spread over the tabletop, the man began asking questions about each item.

"Who is this person? What is this paper for? Where is the rest of your money? Why do you have this item? Who wrote these words? Tell me what this means? Where did you get this business card? Whose phone number is this?

After another hour had passed, Simon's interrogators left him abruptly without any explanation. Moments later a young man brought him a lunch.

Simon ate without tasting, and he wasn't even sure he was digesting. His stomach felt just as squeezed up with fear as his thoughts. Not knowing what would happen to him next was a torture more intense than thirst.

When his two questioning companions returned and began at once asking more questions, it was all Simon could do to stifle a groan. When would it end? What else could he possibly say that he hadn't already said? What did they want from him?

He didn't ask any of those questions though. He continued to answer, and in between his answers he began to pray. "God give me strength for whatever is ahead. Guide my words, Lord." And then, "God please make it stop!"

It was after four o'clock in the afternoon before Simon was escorted from the interrogation room. Joy flushed some of the day's stress from him at the sight of Wesley waiting in the hallway. Neither of them spoke. When they were led down another few hallways and into a small room, Simon collapsed with relief to be finally left alone with Wesley.

"What happened to you? Where did they take you?" Wesley wanted to know.

Simon told Wesley about the room where he had spent the day and some of the questions he was asked. "They asked questions about you, too," Simon admitted.

"What did you say?"

Simon shrugged. "I told the truth," he said. "I just told them everything."

"Me too," Wesley said. "But they just kept asking and asking. I had to keep telling them the same things so many times."

Simon nodded.

For awhile the two compared their experiences and the questions they had been asked. Then they began speculating on what might happen to them.

Wearily Simon leaned his back against the wall and looked intently at the locking mechanism above the door knob. His mind was busy plotting ways in which they might escape the building before they were put in jail or sent back to Romania when the balding man with the fierce, black eyes and the woman interpreter came into their room.

Simon held out his hand to accept the papers the woman was giving each of them.

In the picture he held his own startled looking face staring out at him from a card the woman told him would be his temporary ID. Other papers were vouchers, the woman explained. They would act like money for Simon and Wesley at a certain hostel where they could sleep and eat. More papers were forms to be filled out. This one gave instructions for how they should write out something called a declaration stating their desire to stay in Canada and a history of their life. There were also lists of places and addresses. Other information detailed the process of the immigration hearing and explained about immigration lawyers. They were to apply for a medical card in one place, request forms to apply for a temporary work visa in another, register for language classes somewhere else. In ten days they would be expected to show that they had found a place of residence, and prove that they had completed certain applications and searched for employment. Every few days they would be expected to check in to report on their progress.

Wesley's mouth was open in astonishment and Simon must have looked just as confused. He was listening intently, but he didn't catch much of what the woman was saying. His mind had snagged on the words, "These are the directions to follow to where you will stay."

Could it be that they were being allowed to walk away? Were they really free to go? He could not believe what he was

255

hearing. He'd been busy planning an elaborate escape, and here they were being dismissed, free to go find some type of hotel where this little voucher said they could stay for ten days.

In the hallway once more Simon and Wesley stood by the elevator, where they were directed. It would take them down to the right outside entrance, the woman interpreter told them. For a moment it looked as if the woman was preparing to walk away, then, perhaps sensing their bewilderment, she told them to wait downstairs where she would explain more.

It sounded terribly complicated even once the woman had explained everything again. Simon felt a rush of excitement shoot through him when he finally opened the big glass doors of the custom's building and walked out into the streets of Montreal. By the amount of paperwork he clutched in his hand, he knew they would have a lot of work ahead of them with none of it promising they would be able to stay in Canada. Hundreds applied everyday; the woman had told them. Not all of them would be allowed to stay. The price of freedom had not yet been paid off. A long road lay ahead of them if they hoped to become Canadian citizens, but Simon let optimism sneak inside until something that felt a lot like joy began to fill his heart.

Hadn't God brought them this far? Would He not see them through this next step too? Beside him, Wesley spoke of finding a public phone to call home. He wondered aloud at his surprise of walking free. He exclaimed over the skyscrapers, the sleek American cars and the well–dressed people hurrying past. But Simon had no words. He walked as if within a dream.

Across the road a courtyard of fountains and flowers graced a stately building of carved columns and arching windows. In the sun's slanting evening light, a wall of windows on another building shone with such splendor, it stopped Simon's breath.

When his lungs prompted him to take in air again, he gasped it in like a drowning man, and when he breathed out, his breath came out in a song.

A song that was familiar and more precious to him now. He stopped when Wesley turned to smile at him. And through their breath they sang the song they knew so well... "Because He lives I can face tomorrow..."

It was a song like no other, a song of Hope and Peace.

***

The End

EPILOGUE

From speaking with other Romanian emigrants, Wesley and Simon soon learned that many who had attempted to escape by container had been found dead. The three young men who had been so eager for Wesley to accompany them in a container had all perished.

Simon's own family had been told that he had died.

When Simon phoned his brother Stefan to tell him where he was, an uproar of celebration and noise greeted his call. Friends of Stefan's were visiting Simon's brother to console him because Stefan believed that Simon was dead. Stefan urged Simon to phone their parents right away. Officials had recently told Simon's parents that their youngest son had tried to escape in a container and had not survived. Simon's family had been mourning him for five days already when he called, and it took a few moments to convince them that he was really alive.

Wesley's sister was already off work at the library so Wesley contacted a neighbor who had a telephone in order to pass along the message that he had arrived safely in Canada.

Although they were alive and safe, the price of freedom continued to be expensive during Wesley and Simon's first few weeks in Montreal. Many hardships still lay ahead of them, and both young men suffered the effects of their harrowing experience for some time. Wesley promptly contracted an extreme case of chicken pox and then developed a serious lung infection that prevented him from working. Simon endured days of suffering after their ordeal because his lower intestines had quit functioning. He required medical care shortly after they arrived.

Everything was new and strange. With no knowledge of French or English, it was difficult to find their way about the huge city of Montreal and fulfill the requirements demanded by immigration.

Fellow Romanian immigrants, also applying for Canadian citizenship, and the only persons who spoke their language, discouraged Simon and Wesley by telling them they were sure to be sent back home because they had said all the wrong things during their initial interrogation. They told them that they should have lied, and told their interrogators that they suffered police beatings daily, that they were orphans with no family or means of support in Romania. They led Simon and Wesley to feel they now had little chance of being allowed to stay.

The many forms and obligations took a great deal of time and effort to complete as well. Line-ups were long everywhere they went to apply for their required temporary papers and permits. Work and an affordable apartment proved difficult to find, but Simon and Wesley did not complain. There was a tremendous amount of running around, and daily frustrations, but the people who dealt with them "treated them like human beings," as Simon observed. They seemed to care about their welfare and were genuinely concerned that they would have a place to sleep, or enough to eat.

Within two weeks of their arrival, Simon and Wesley were fortunate to find employment, working for a Romanian property manager in Montreal. They found an apartment they could afford, located a church where they began singing together, employed an immigration lawyer, and even began to make payments on an older car. Their employer gradually promoted them both to greater responsibility and favor as he realized that he had found two honest, hard workers.

Wesley and Simon were still concerned that they could be deported. Around them they constantly heard of people who had been refused entrance into Canada. They heard of others who were abusing the system by paying women to marry them just to become landed immigrants. Others lied about their situation to obtain extra money from Human Resources or special consideration from the authorities. When word spread of a Romanian run logging camp, Simon and Wesley decided to drive into the remote wilderness area to apply for work there. Wages were high in the logging business and they would be able to earn more money, they reasoned. Escape would be easier from such a remote location, too. Perhaps they would try to cross the border into the United States if they were ordered to leave. They would not risk being sent back to Romania. If their application into Canada were turned down, they planned to disappear somewhere in an attempt to remain free.

Neither Simon nor Wesley were prepared for the extreme lifestyles of those who lived in remote logging camps. Although the mosquitoes were unbearable and the accommodations were crude, it was the drugs, the drinking and the type of men who worked in the logging camps that persuaded both young men that this was not a good place for them.

Providentially, another option opened up for Wesley as soon as they returned to Montreal. A Christian couple from Kelowna, British Columbia (BC), had met Wesley's family while visiting in Romania. They tracked Wesley down in Montreal by telephone and asked him if he would like to come to British Columbia.

The offer came from a Christian Romanian speaking family, and Wesley, although he knew nothing of what British

Columbia was like or even where it was, felt genuinely grateful for the offer. He would not consider going without Simon though. The two were a team.

When Wesley was told a few days later that Simon was welcome to come along, the two quickly made up their minds to take the chance.

Neither of them ever regretted the decision to travel west.

On their second weekend in BC, the family who had brought them to Kelowna heard them singing in their downstairs suite, where Wesley and Simon were asked if they would be willing to sing at camp meeting scheduled to begin in Hope, B.C. in a few days.

From that first singing debut at camp meeting 1999, Simon and Wesley have been allowing God to use their voices in a ministry of song and story in many places.

Simon & Wesley Singing

In Kelowna, the two quickly made good friends, found work, enrolled in classes to learn English and enjoyed being adopted into a loving church family. But daily they carried the fear of being sent back to Romania. The immigration process became their greatest nightmare, and a stressful procession of problems and complications threatened to dash their hopes of ever becoming Canadians.

When a letter came telling Simon and Wesley that a date had been set for their "final" immigration hearing in Montreal, the two were confused because they had not yet been given a *first* hearing. With a rental car, they drove to Montreal only to hear the worst possible news their case had been closed. The summons for them to appear in person in a Montreal court had only one purpose they were to receive the official verdict, which was: a denial to enter the country, and an order to return to their homeland.

Fortunately God intervened in Wesley and Simon's lives once more. The immigration lawyer they had first employed, and who had unjustly closed their case, was replaced with another lawyer who spoke on their behalf. And the judge at their hearing allowed their case to be re opened an unprecedented decision in the world of immigration law.

Over the next few months Simon and Wesley, with the help of their Montreal immigration lawyer, worked tirelessly to gather information that would influence their case. Personal letters of character guarantee and recommendation were solicited from family, friends and pastors in Romania, in Italy, Montreal and British Columbia.

Because they were pleading asylum from Romania on the basis of their faith, Simon and Wesley were stunned when their lawyer directed them to go to the library and read about Romanian law. In glaring print they read that all Romanians were free to practice the religion of their choice without persecution. Even though they both knew such a law was not upheld in their homeland it was stated in the constitution! Persecution for one's religion occurred regularly, but how could they hope to contradict the official declarations in a book of law? If the judge deemed that law valid, they would not see any reason why Simon and Wesley could not return to Romania to serve their term of military duty.

Worry and a constant feeling of insecurity threatened their faith many times during the next few months while Simon and Wesley prepared for their next court hearing in Vancouver.

On several occasions people who had experience in immigration discouraged them further with conflicting stories and advice. And once again they looked around anxiously at the friends they had made and the lives they were building knowing they were becoming too attached and fearing they would soon have to leave it all behind.

On September 7, 2000, Simon and Wesley stood before three judges, an interpreter, and their lawyer in a Vancouver courthouse.

It felt more like an interrogation than it did a hearing. Questioned separately, both Simon and Wesley were drilled once more on the same questions they had originally been asked back in Montreal, the day they left the ship, along with hundreds of new questions. The judges wanted to know every detail of their lives and their friend's lives and their day to day habits of living.

Question after question centered on their religion. How could they prove that their faith was not just something they were using to plead religious persecution? How often did they attend church? Had they attended church during their three months in Montreal? Why did they get baptized in Italy and not earlier, in Romania? Wasn't it possible to serve their military duty and remain faithful to their God?

Hadn't hundreds of others managed to survive both? (In reality it's one, or the other.)

At one point their lawyer asked for the dismissal of their Romanian interpreter when he realized that the man had not been relaying Simon and Wesley's words accurately.

Simon and Wesley felt extremely grateful that their lawyer had prepared him self and them so diligently and seemed so determined to win their case. They were both growing weary and a little discouraged, though, as the morning stretched into midday and then dragged on into late afternoon. On the few breaks that they were allowed to be together the two knelt and prayed earnestly. In Kelowna, and many other locations, family, friends and church family members were doing the same.

At three o'clock, the building closed its doors. Everyone left their offices to go home except the judges dealing with Simon and Wesley's case. In their courtroom the hearing continued with question upon question.

Soon after five p.m. both Wesley and Simon were asked to come back into the courtroom to listen as one judge read out a lengthy declaration of their experiences and their application for entrance into Canada.

The words, *"You are granted landed immigrant status,"* took them both by surprise. When the judges stepped down to mingle and speak personally with each of them, it was another surprise. One judge admitted that, in spite of the questions that she had asked, she knew about the situation in Romania. She realized that the law concerning religious persecution was not upheld. Another judge commended both Wesley and Simon for their faith and their integrity.

Since applicants usually had to wait weeks or longer for a formal letter in the mail to know the results of their immigration hearing, everyone seemed in shock that a decision had been reached on the same day as the hearing.

Prayer made the difference according to Simon and Wesley. They count the outcome in that courtroom as another miracle to add to their list of God's intervention in their lives.

Today, Wesley and Simon's greatest passion is to share their faith and their incredible story in song. Since their arrival, Simon and Wesley have been singing, and in 2003 they began to combine their voices in a quartet called the "**Freedom Singers**".

(The group included Don Melashenko, his wife Marilyn Melashenko as accompanist, and Christopher Dupuis, who was more recently replaced by Donavan Diminyatz)

Freedom Singers

On January 15, 2004 Wesley Pop and Simon Ivascu were granted Canadian citizenship and in August 2004, with legal passports in hand, they were able to travel back to Romania to visit family and friends.

**Pictures of Wesley & Simon
receiving their Canadian citizenship**

Even after paying such a high price for their freedom, Simon and Wesley both struggle at times to accept and feel that they are truly free. After so many years of being afraid and distrustful, freedom is not an easy thing to grasp. Sometimes they still find themselves wary, doubting they will be treated fairly or becoming tense in front of authorities.

Neither have any doubts about God, however. Their faith is strong.

Ask Simon and Wesley if they believe that they were lucky to have survived such an ordeal, and they will both answer, *"No."*

Luck did not play a part in their experience with God, according to Wesley or Simon. They don't believe in luck they believe in miracles. And everyday they thank God for the miracle of their survival and the opportunities to live and sing for God's glory.

***

About the Authors

Simon and Wesley,

We're thrilled that your amazing story has at last become book form. It is such a testimony to the greatness of our God Who is always ready and willing to send yet another miracle our way. As compelling as your story is, we have found your hearts to be even more so, and are excited to see God touch lives through this book. God bless!

Marc and Jill Stickle

Over the many years of serving my Lord and Savior, I have been blessed to work alongside many God fearing and loving people, two of which I sincerely consider are Simon and Wesley. Their tenacity, determination and gumption, but above all their faith in the Lord Jesus has been a blessing and source of courage to my life. Your story and your testimony I know will touch millions of lives, as we Christians must be reminded daily of who we must surrender to no matter the situation.

Pastor Paul Antunes

In a society that has grown accustomed to performance and sophistication, Simon and Wesley have brought an invigorating sense of truth to the music and ministry that they share. No doubt their youth spent in the repressive communist environment of Romania made the expression of freedom found in Jesus Christ a special Joy, at least it would seem so as one listens to their passionate renditions of old gospel favorites. With the clear tones of their music and life, I have been moved to reexamine my own view of God. With an outlook on life that includes the medicine of a merry heart, Simon and Wes have made us all friends of theirs, and each other to.

Theirs is a testimony of what God will do with young men, willing to follow His lead wherever that may be! I and the congregations I pastor have been blessed so much by their music and their friendship. I know that you will be lifted as you read their story, in their words, and share the wonder of their God, who can deliver from trouble, in trouble, the Joy Unspeakable, the Life more abundant.

Pastor Peter Ford

Dedication

**We dedicate this book
to our families and friends who
supported us with their prayers...**

**Many thanks to Oltean's, Melashenko's,
Tataryn's, Thorp's and the Otto/Ferster Family for
being our family here in Canada...**

**We also want to thank Bev-Ellen Clarke for
her dedication in co-writing the book with us.
Thank-you for recapturing the many
trials and miracles of our journey.**

**Many thanks to Ralph Kneller
for the title of our book.**

God Bless you All

Love Simon & Wesley